PATSY JEFFERSON
Of Monticello

Also by Marguerite Vance

✤

A STAR FOR HANSI

MARTA

CAPITALS OF THE WORLD

PAULA

PAULA GOES AWAY TO SCHOOL

WHILE SHEPHERDS WATCHED

MARTHA, DAUGHTER OF VIRGINIA

Patsy Jefferson

PATSY JEFFERSON

of Monticello

By MARGUERITE VANCE

Illustrated by Nedda Walker

E. P. DUTTON & COMPANY, INC.

NEW YORK

FOR JOHN

CONTENTS

ACKNOWLEDGMENT

For help in preparing my manuscript I make grateful acknowledgment to the following:

JEFFERSON AND MONTICELLO
By Paul Wilstach
Doubleday & Company

THE DOMESTIC LIFE OF THOMAS JEFFERSON
By Sarah N. Randolph
Harper Brothers

MY HEAD AND MY HEART
A Little History of Thomas Jefferson and Maria Cosway
By Helen Duprey Bullock
G. P. Putnam's Sons

LIFE AND TIMES OF THOMAS JEFFERSON
By Thomas Watson
Dodd, Mead & Company

THE YOUNG JEFFERSON
By Claude G. Bowers
Houghton Mifflin Co.

VIRGINIA QUARTERLY
January, 1931
Article by Dumas Malone

MODES AND MANNERS — EIGHTEENTH CENTURY
By Max von Boehn
E. P. Dutton & Co., Inc.

THOMAS JEFFERSON
By Frank and Cortelle Hutchins
Longmans, Green & Co.

FIRST LADIES
By Kathleen Prindiville
Macmillan Company

WE VISIT OLD INNS
By Mary Harrod Northend
Small

OLD BOSTON IN COLONIAL DAYS
By Mary Caroline Crawford
L. C. Page & Company

PAUL REVERE AND THE WORLD HE LIVED IN
By Esther Forbes
Houghton Mifflin Co.

GUIDE PRATIQUE A TRAVERS LE VIEUX PARIS
By Edouard Champion (ed.)

THOMAS JEFFERSON, AMI DE LA REVOLUTION FRANCAISE
(Thèse pour le doctorat d'Université à la Faculté des Lettres de Grenoble par George H. McKee)

MARIE ANTOINETTE
By Stefan Zweig
Viking Press

SAILING SHIPS AND THEIR STORY
Edward K. Chatterton
J. B. Lippincott Company

AUTHOR'S FOREWORD

As in the case of its predecessor, MARTHA, DAUGHTER OF VIRGINIA, the primary purpose of this book has been to give its main characters substance and spirit in the eyes and minds of those who read about them.

No one can be absolutely certain of the day-by-day activities of these people who lived so long ago; one can, however, by combining imagination and common sense, arrive within hailing distance of fact. Thus is this a "story" as contrasted to a biography. Basic dates and facts have been held to faithfully, but where source material failed to fill in certain gaps of time and experience I have resorted to fiction, keeping it always logical and as consistent as possible with known fact. To take any unwarranted liberty with the life-story of Thomas Jefferson's beloved Patsy is farthest from my thought, and what fictionizing there may be in this story I trust will not detract from the work as a whole which, to the best of my knowledge, does follow the pattern of simple, unadorned fact.

M. V.

PATSY JEFFERSON
OF MONTICELLO

Chapter 1

AWAY, AWAY, TO ANOTHER LAND!

THE weather, as befitted the weather of July, was uncomfortably warm on the morning of July 5, 1784. The air was heavy with the sweetish smell of kelp and tar and the penetrating odor of fish in brine. The sun beat down on the Boston docks with a ferocity that set heat waves shimmering and dancing in the brassy light. Overhead and far away, the sky stretched in an endless arch of blue-white haze.

On the deck of the good ship *Ceres,* a young girl wearing a traveling dress of serviceable dark green silk, sat on a deck stool and shaded her eyes with her hand as she looked

15

anxiously up and down the wharf. Her gray-green eyes took on a deeper hue from the green brocaded bonnet she wore tied by a voluminous bow under her pointed little chin, and she bit her lip to keep that chin from quivering.

At twelve, Martha Jefferson knew no well-bred young lady wept in public, and what could be more public than the main deck of Mr. Nathaniel Tracy's handsome vessel, the *Ceres?* Martha swallowed hard and touched her upper lip with a folded pocket handkerchief. Perspiration stood in beads along her forehead, too, and she longed to untie the heavy bonnet ribbons and to strip the long, tight mitts of tucked linen from her arms. Instead, she sat quietly, alternately watching the wheeling gulls overhead and the busy wharf where momentarily she knew her father must appear, threading his way easily among the shouting carters and draymen. A red-brown curl, caught by a sudden gust, whipped out from under the bonnet and Martha tucked it carefully back.

"Seem like Mas' Tom'd be comin' soon now, don't it, Miss Patsy?" a soft voice spoke beside her.

Martha stood up. "He'll he here now soon, Callie." There was a sharp note of anxiety in her voice but, old for her years, she remembered to mask her fears before the Negress. Though her adoring guardian for the moment,

the simple, kindly old woman looked upon her twelve-year-old charge as a lady of incalculable wisdom, a personage capable of averting any difficulty. From experience Callie knew that her "white folks" understood the ways of their world. Miss Patsy might be a bit worried because Mas' Tom was so long in coming, but it was a different kind of worry from Callie's deep and terrible anxiety over the sea voyage upon which she was embarking. A little white lady's worry was like a tiny prick from a rose thorn; a slave woman's fear was a wind roaring out of an inky sky. You could stop the thorn's sting, but before the wind you were helpless.

"There he is! There's Papa!" Martha's voice rose gayly above the whine of hand winches and the shouts of sailors.

Thomas Jefferson, hat in hand, powdered hair blowing back from a broad, high forehead, strode up the gangplank and crossed the deck to Martha's side. A whimsical smile played about his rather thin lips. Perhaps he was recalling how, at *Monticello,* his beloved eldest daughter always had come flying to meet him after even a short absence. Now she stood smiling, eager, hands outstretched, yet waiting for him to come to her.

Two years with Mrs. Hopkinson in Philadelphia had accomplished a great deal for the timid, homesick, little girl from Virginia. Weeping came easily to Patsy in those early years, and rebellion at discipline from anyone but her father made teaching her no sinecure.

Now, serene, poised even in the withering heat, Martha Jefferson laughed in joyous relief as she watched her father's tall figure striding toward her.

Callie murmured, "Bless de Lohd!" and bobbed a curtsy, a gesture to her intense gratitude to Providence for her "Mas' Tom's" return.

"Did you find them, Papa? Did the carter lose his way? Did you search far?" The questions jostled one another for first place.

Jefferson mopped his hot face with an enormous white handkerchief and patted Martha's shoulder. "Yes, dear, I found our luggage safe and sound," he answered. "The poor fellow had taken a wrong turn coming down to the dock and though he was only a stone's throw from the ship here, he could not somehow find an open lane to reach it. All's well now. Our boxes are safely aboard. This one," he grinned like a sheepish schoolboy and patted an oblong case under his arm, "this I trust to no one."

"Oh, your fiddle, Papa! I'm so glad we have it. 'Twill be like home to hear it." Martha touched the shining case lovingly.

"Mm, yes. But let's get out of this hot sun, my Patsy. Have you seen Colonel Tracy? Has Captain St. Barbé been by? Here Callie, you, too, come over into the shade. Ah, here comes Colonel Tracy now."

As the group moved to a cooler spot, they were joined by a gentleman whose bearing and fine attire proclaimed him a man of affluence and position. Smallclothes of light-weight blue worsted were topped by a frilled shirt of finest white China silk. Silver buckles glittered on the cockade of his hat, at his knees and on his square-toed pumps. With a sharp little catch of breath, Martha noted a heavy gold ring with a huge garnet set in it, worn on his thumb. She recalled having heard the girls at school say that thumb rings were being worn by many Court gentlemen abroad. Now here was one on the thumb of a plain American colonel! Martha realized suddenly that she was staring, and looked away.

"Welcome to the *Ceres,* Mr. Jefferson," Colonel Tracy was saying as he shook the noted Virginian's hand. "And this," turning to study Martha with friendly, gray eyes, "I suppose is Miss Jefferson?" He shook hands with her in turn, and Martha liked his smile, his deep, pleasant voice.

"Captain St. Barbé and I are deeply honored," he continued.

"On the other hand," laughed Thomas Jefferson, "my daughter and I are the ones to feel signally honored. I hear the *Ceres* is carrying only six passengers, and you have permitted us to constitute one half of your passenger list! You are kind, indeed."

Captain St. Barbé, a tall, ruddy-faced man with a booming voice, now joined them. His attention was all on Martha. He smiled, looking from her to her father.

"Her father's daughter," he rumbled, patting her arm. "Mr. Jefferson here," he addressed Colonel Tracy, "left Miss Martha and her servant in my charge an hour ago while he went in search of some lost luggage. An old salt like me recognizes self-discipline when he encounters it. I passed Miss Martha from time to time as she sat yonder, and never, by so much as a turn of the head, did she betray her fear lest we sail without her father. And I knew by her expression she felt it. Come now, child, you know I'm right. That, I call magnificent self-control, magnificent!"

He slapped his thigh and squinted at the sun, and the laughter of the other two men and Martha's embarrassment were lost in his next words: "We're off! I'll hope to see you at dinner." He wheeled and strode toward the poop deck. A whistle blew, the gangplank came up and, following the shout, "Man the windlass!" there came the steady clank-clink-clank of windlass pawls as the anchor lifted. Shore lines were cast off.

Fascinated, Martha moved a step closer to her father,

watching the snowy sails unfurl. Behind her, Callie made a small sound, half sob, half exclamation of wonder. Slowly, slowly the graceful ship moved away from the pier. A breeze fluttered the sails and they ballooned suddenly outward and upward, white clouds against a summer-blue .sky. The *Ceres* headed toward the open sea.

The beautiful vessel, pride of its owner and of its captain, had much to recommend it. In a day when sleeping quarters for passengers were usually in stuffy cubicles beneath the poop deck, the *Ceres* boasted a "Great Cabbin" situated slightly below the main deck in the stern, with "bed places" or staterooms opening into it.

To her delight, Martha saw a small window beside her berth, hooks for her clothes, a washstand with pewter pitcher and bowl. A pallet for Callie, like a trundle bed, was pushed beneath the berth. Martha could hear her father in the adjoining cabin, unstrapping boxes, shaking out the wrinkles in his greatcoat.

She sighed happily and slowly untied her bonnet ribbons and let the heavy bonnet slide back. A cool breeze from the window touched her damp, copper-colored curls and hot cheeks. Suddenly tired after weeks of travel, Martha sat down on the berth, watching Callie lay out brushes and soap and hand-loomed towels marked with a beautifully wrought "J."

Away, Away to Another Land

Mother had loved to embroider, Martha recalled, and had taught her to make the tiny, even stitches. All during that last summer, two years ago, they had sat so often together on the cool, shady gallery at *Monticello,* hemstitching napkins, embroidering just such "J's" on towels and pillowcases.

They had had long talks there, looking out on the woodland, listening to the drowsy summer sounds, talks which Martha was to remember with poignant sadness whenever she heard the call of a pewit or the rush of wind through tall pines. For when autumn came, the frail, lovely mother was gone. Baby sister Lucy Elizabeth, Polly who was four, and Martha, just ten, were left. Two years ago. Sometimes it seemed ever so much longer.

Callie continued to unpack and set the cabin to rights. Martha roused herself, realizing the breeze had grown strong and that beneath her feet a gentle motion, up — down — up — down, marked the stately progress of the *Ceres* before the wind.

For a less courageous girl of that day such a voyage would have held almost unbearable terrors. Pirates, unscrupulous and cruel, were not uncommon. Storms gravely menaced all sailing ships, and many a jaunty barkentine that sailed from Boston Harbor disappeared over the horizon never to be heard from again. Had she "run under" in a hurricane? Had she been attacked, scuttled, and sent to the bottom by pirates? One solemn conjecture was as good as another.

Martha, if she gave much thought to these dangers, kept her misgivings to herself. She was on her way to France with "Papa" whose beloved comrade she was. What mattered the weather or threat of pirates?

MUSIC IN THE AFTERNOON

OFTEN, as they had covered the miles between Philadelphia and Boston, Martha marvelled how, in spite of the many weighty matters on his mind, this beloved father of hers seemed never to lack time for friendliness and understanding toward all people with whom he came in contact. It was, she found, one of the outstanding characteristics which all his life endeared him to his fellow men.

25

Patsy Jefferson of Monticello

Young Thomas Jefferson, tall, handsome, red-headed, was twenty-nine years old when on a January day in 1772 he brought his bride, Martha Wayles Skelton, to their mountain top home, *Monticello,* five miles east of Charlottesville in Albermarle County, Virginia. Well-to-do in his own right, he found his modest fortune doubled the year following his marriage by his wife's legacy from her father. This legacy included forty thousand acres of land and a hundred and thirty-five slaves.

The mansion on the mountain top, though perhaps never actually completed in the meticulous eyes of Jefferson, was by that time an impressive dwelling reached by winding drives and bridle paths through the forest.

Mrs. Jefferson was not only a noted beauty but a skilled and gracious home-maker as well. With her young husband, she walked or rode over the vast plantation which seemed to stretch to the horizon. She directed the planting of the herb garden and persuaded the gardeners that hepatica and meadowsweet were as lovely in a garden as in the forest. She exclaimed in delighted wonder at the deer and elk moving through the shadows of the park, and when evening came, dark head bent over her sewing, she listened while Jefferson read aloud from the classics they both loved. Again, they discussed a particularly difficult case which

Music in the Afternoon

Jefferson, as a prominent lawyer and member of the House of Burgesses, was handling; or they pored over blueprints of parts of the mansion still under construction. Theirs was a perfect companionship, perfect happiness.

In the autumn a daughter was born and named Martha for her mother. Oddly enough, like Martha Dandridge who became Martha Washington, little Martha Jefferson was given by her father the nickname "Patsy." Possibly it was a common nickname for Martha at that time. Again, the young Jeffersons undoubtedly were on the most friendly terms with the Dandridge-Custis-Washington families and may have given their baby the nickname in a spirit of gay affection. History does not tell us and it is unimportant.

Martha was just a year old when six cousins, the Dabney Carr children, came to make their home at *Monticello*. Their mother was Thomas Jefferson's widowed sister; their father, Dabney Carr, had been his closest boyhood friend.

Mary was a new baby; Jane, two years old; Virginia, three. The boys were Dabney Jr., a round-faced little boy of six; Samuel, seven; and Peter the oldest, the "big cousin," was nine. Martha, toddling about among them in high glee at so much company, was a favorite. To Jane and Virginia, babies themselves, she was just another sister. The boys, feeling very grown up and superior, stood a little aloof from so much feminine babyhood and played their own games.

Meanwhile, important changes were taking place, changes which eventually would greatly influence the lives of all the children at *Monticello*.

The First Continental Congress met in Philadelphia early in the autumn that Martha and her six cousins celebrated her second birthday with a tea party on the gallery. That autumn, too, the children heard that "Uncle Tom" had given up his law practice, had turned it over to "Cousin Edmund" Randolph.

Thomas Jefferson loved his country and the ideals for which it stood with a fervor equalled by few men. That beloved country was now being outraged and baited by the stupid monarch of the motherland, England. Strong men were needed to guide the American Colonies, for if war came, they must be ready. To such men as George Washington and quiet, thoughtful Thomas Jefferson, and fiery Patrick Henry fell much of the burden of uniting the Colonies for the task ahead.

Martha was not quite three when, on a May morning in 1775, she stood beside her mother on the gallery, waving her father off to Williamsburg, the Virginia capital. From there he would travel north to Philadelphia, a journey of ten days by coach, where the second Continental Congress would be in session. There was the sound of musketry rattling across the land. The Continental Army had been formed and George Washington had been elected Commander in Chief.

In August, Jefferson was back at *Monticello* where more and ever more building was in progress on the mansion itself, on the slave quarters, on the beautiful grounds. Though war had come, it still seemed remote from the peaceful Virginia countryside. But one part of the house was kept quiet. Mrs. Jefferson was ill — very ill.

Often lonely and restless, despite her six playmates, little Martha would slip away from them and from her nurse. Forbidden to go to the part of the house where building was in progress, she would carry her best loved wooden doll to a corner of the bottom step of the flight leading from the verandah to the drive. Here she would sit, her doll hugged close, rocking slowly back and forth, forward and back, crooning a tuneless lullaby. And here she sat on a certain August morning.

Dotted across the lawn, a flock of sheep moved slowly, cropping the grass. The air was sweet with the smell of sun-warmed earth and foliage; larks wheeled and darted across the sky, singing.

Martha watched them, squinting a little in the sun,

then turned her head. Country child that she was, she discerned faint noises which to a city child would have been indistinguishable from other outdoor sounds. Now, far down the bridle path which wound for miles around the *Monticello* estate, she heard the rhythmic, unhurried put-a-put, put-a-put of approaching hoof beats. Nearer, nearer they sounded, and now, rounding the bend, a solitary rider came toward her.

Martha sat, small hands clasped on her doll's back as it lay, face down across her lap, watching the approaching rider. Even at three Martha was not a timid child. Her large gray-green eyes regarded him quietly and with interest. Then, as though some hidden spring had been released, the doll clattered to the ground as Martha flew to meet the rider. His mount snorted and danced as the little figure, skirts flying, hurtled toward it down the drive. Its rider reined it in, then quickly swung down from the saddle.

"Patsy! Patsy, girl!" He held out his arms and she ran into them.

"Papa! My Papa!" Martha buried her face in his stock and wound her arms around his neck. Her father held her close and kissed her warm little cheek. The horse, in friendly welcome, bent its fine head and whuffled softly against her curls.

Music in the Afternoon

For only a moment they stood so, each a completely happy being. To each it was a perfect segment out of time. Then running feet along the drive. . . .

"Mas' Tom! Howdy, Mas' Tom!" A groom led away the horse.

From the verandah a soft voice: "Tom Jefferson! Well, upon my word! Welcome home!"

Still holding Martha in his arms, Jefferson started toward the verandah, then turned to call after the groom:

"Oh, Jake, be careful of that case tied to the saddle, please. It's a violin. Bring it to my room when you've unsaddled, will you?"

The boy bobbed his assent. Jefferson hurried up the steps and stooped to kiss his sister, Mrs. Carr. Martha slid to the ground but still clung to her father's hand. With a little stab of jealousy, she realized they had forgotten her, they were talking of other matters. Jefferson was hearing that his wife, though somewhat improved, was still very sick; that baby Jane, the eighteen-months-old toddler, ill of a teething fever, was growing weaker.

"But," Mrs. Carr added philosophically, "remember, Tom, this is the sickly season. August through September has ever been a bad time in the South. Let an autumn breeze blow up from the Chesapeake and methinks both Martha and Janie will be well again."

Patsy Jefferson of Monticello

Of that 'sickly season' Martha was to remember two things but dimly and one which all her life she loved to look back upon. She remembered her mother, after a while, wan and lovely, and so fragile that Martha eyed her from a distance in awed adoration, returned to the family circle. Leaning on her husband's arm, Mrs. Jefferson strolled across the lawn in the pleasant cool of evening, and Martha, still a little shy, worshiping from afar, trotted beside her father, her hand fast in his.

Then one day Janie was no longer there. Martha could never recall just how she knew it, but the knowledge was dimly part of that strange, late summer. The third memory of that season, like a favorite chord of music, or the illusive, sweet smell of wood smoke on a certain country morning, remained in Martha's heart forever.

On the late afternoon of her father's arrival at *Monticello,* she woke from her nap to hear faint, shining, fairy sounds coming from somewhere nearby. She slipped from the bed and, barefooted, ran down the passage and out into the great hall. Here the lovely sound was fainter. Martha turned and retraced her steps. Off the passage, beyond the dining room, giving on the terrace, was a room known as the tea room. Through the dining room Martha was drawn by the music until, at the door of the tea room, she stopped. Her father stood before a music rack, playing a violin, his

brow puckered as he concentrated on the notes. His shoulders moved to the rhythm of the music, and Martha's own small body began to sway as she stood watching, listening, enchanted.

The piece finished, Jefferson lowered the violin and saw the little shift-clad figure in the doorway, hands clasped in wonder and delight.

He laid the instrument down and went to stoop before the child. "Did you like it, Patsy?" he asked, drawing her to him. And Martha, standing in the circle of his arms, nodded happily. "Play more, Papa," she whispered.

Jefferson lifted the little girl to a seat in one of the chairs facing the terrace and again took up his violin. The green-and-gold light of the late summer afternoon flooded the room with cool shadows; music, as gay, as tremulous as the dancing reflection of sunlight on water, drifted out to meet the woodland sounds from the garden. At *Monticello* Thomas Jefferson was playing for Patsy. The experience, combined of sight and sound and sweet late-summer smells, was to remain with her always.

Autumn came and Christmas and the New Year — 1776 — with the happy family of boys and girls romping in the nursery and about the grounds of *Monticello*.

Meanwhile, in Philadelphia in the State House on Chestnut Street, Thomas Jefferson and the other members

Music in the Afternoon

of the Congress waited and worked and hoped and prayed that a way might yet be found to avert total war with the homeland, England.

In January, tired and discouraged, he came home for a visit and it was early May before again he returned to Philadelphia. Peter, Sam and Dabney each had his saddle horse by this time, and Martha day after day watched with stormy eyes as the boys galloped away beside their uncle on their morning rides.

There were five thousand acres of mountain, valley, wood, and field over which to ride and still not cross the boundaries of the *Monticello* estate. Small wonder the boys loved their home and the tall, distinguished uncle whose generosity provided it.

One morning, shortly before his return to Philadelphia, Thomas Jefferson lingered on the gallery talking with his wife and Mrs. Carr while waiting for the horses to be brought around. The three boys, impatient to be off, tossed pebbles in the driveway. A little apart, Virginia Carr showed her sister Jane and her cousin Martha the sampler she had begun the day before. Mrs. Jefferson was better, and from her deep chair in a sunny spot, was enjoying the sweet spring air.

Two grooms, each leading two horses, came along the drive. The boys ran to meet them and swung themselves up into their saddles. Only Dabney required the help of a groom to give him a "leg up." Jefferson finished the anecdote he was telling the ladies and turned, still laughing, to descend to the drive, when the group of little girls caught his eye.

Martha, her coppery curls bobbing from beneath her pretty, ruffled mobcap, eyes turned on her father, had lost interest in Virginia's sampler. If only — if only! A great wish grew and grew in her heart until it threatened to suffocate her. Something of that wish must have communicated itself to Jefferson. He smiled down at the children, drawing on his gloves. "Methinks so fine a morning calls for company on a ride," he observed. "How would my Patsy like to ride with me? What do you say, Mamma?" He turned to his wife.

Martha was already on her feet, her thin little face aglow.

Mrs. Jefferson gently demurred. "But, Tom, she's only a baby. 'Twill wear the child out."

"Baby she may be," the father rejoined, his rather severe face still beaming in anticipation, "but enough of her father's daughter to love a ride on horseback, eh, Patsy girl?"

Martha's blue hooded cape was tied about her shoulders, and she knew the dizzying, delicious terror of being lifted to a seat in front of her father on his big roan hunter. For just a moment fright gripped her, then she wriggled to a firmer seat and leaned back, safe and secure. Her father's gloved fingers on the bridle reins behind which she sat, the horse's arched neck before her, the rocking-chair motion of its gait as it carried her, this was adventure.

The child found herself listening to the music made by the wind as it drummed against the silk lining of her hood. There had been another sound like it somewhere once and, watching the blue May sky through a moving tangle of forest branches, she remembered violin music in the tea room. Then, as now, her father had given her pleasure, deep and unforgettable. Martha was too young to realize it, but the bond of beautiful companionship and understanding between these two which was to mean so much in future years was being forged in her babyhood. Martha Jefferson all her life through was her father's idol and he hers.

Shortly after Martha's first horseback ride, her father returned to Philadelphia. There, during the warm days of June, in a little house on the outskirts of the city, he drafted the most important document in American History — the Declaration of Independence. On July 4th it was adopted by the Congress. America was no longer a group of English colonies. It was an independent nation.

Patsy Jefferson of Monticello

The year 1776 passed, then 1777. Thomas Jefferson during these years brought about several great changes in the laws of Virginia. One of these was the old English inheritance law under which a man's eldest son always inherited the father's entire property. This was changed so that a man might divide his property among his children as he chose. Another law which Jefferson was instrumental in changing was that under which slaves could be imported to this country. Now the importation of slaves to Virginia was prohibited.

A few months before Martha's sixth birthday — in August, 1778 — a baby sister was born and named Mary. From the beginning, however, everyone called the little girl Polly.

To the Carr children Polly was just another baby, but to Martha she was the most beautiful being in the world. And, as she grew older, Polly *was* beautiful, with her mother's deep blue eyes and dark curls, her quick laughter and winsome manners. Martha, always tall for her age, with a generous sprinkling of freckles across her high-bridged, aristocratic nose and cheek bones, knew no pangs of jealousy. "Little Sistah" was her pride and her delight.

Life at *Monticello* became gayer, more exciting. Mrs. Jefferson, quite recovered, played her Forte-piano and sang

Music in the Afternoon

with the children; now and then the Eppes cousins from *Eppington* on the lower James came to visit and there were endless games of "tag" and "blind man's buff" and "hide and seek." And once, for a few brief hours, a handsome distant cousin, Thomas Mann Randolph, stopped by with his father to pay his respects. Though several years older than Martha, he played "bean bag" with her and gravely accepted her gift of a kitten at parting. For an hour after he left, Martha wondered wistfully if he had really been serious about coming to *Monticello* again soon. Then she forgot him.

In 1779 the war came suddenly nearer and in a most unusual way. Many Hessians, officer-prisoners captured by the Continental Army, were sent to a concentration camp near Charlottesville. The kindly Virginians opened their homes to them, and the children at *Monticello* watched and listened, open-mouthed, as Thomas Jefferson entertained these newcomers with their guttural speech and stiff Teutonic manners. With this one he played duets; to that one he loaned his precious books for, said he, "The great cause which divides our countries is not to be decided by individual animosities."*

Mrs. Jefferson was no less hospitable and the officers"

* These were Thomas Jefferson's words written to a British officer, General Phillips.

wives found her generous in passing on to them some of her favorite recipes, and just as graciously trying some of theirs in return.

One of these ladies filled Martha with a terror she could not control though she tried to sincerely. This was the Baroness de Riedesel, wife of the Hessian General de Riedesel. The baroness was a huge woman with a thunderous voice, who rode horseback astride, a thing unknown in those days, and came charging up the mountain almost daily either to deliver one of her own delicious *kaffe kuchens*, fresh from the oven, or to borrow a bit of ribwort for tea.

One day, striding across the great hall at *Monticello,* the baroness spied Martha at the foot of the narrow stairs leading up to the nursery.

"*Ach, Frauleinchein,*" she cried, beaming down on the little girl, "do not run away! I think some day we must ask the *mutter* if you cannot come with me to Germany after this so *schrecklich* war is ended. *Nein?*"

Martha took one step up, looking back over her shoulder. "No — no, ma'am," she faltered politely. "My mamma and my papa would not like me to go. And Little Sistah — no, ma'am, thank you. I could not do that."

She did not wait for the good-natured laugh that greeted her solemn little speech. Martha trudged up the stairs as quickly as her high-heeled, morocco shoes would take her. Go to that strange country, Germany? Leave *Monticello?* Oh, never, never! And though Martha's parents explained carefully how well-meaning the baroness had been, she had only to see the lady's big horse come puffing and blowing up the path, and she would vanish to the farthest, most unlikely corner of the house.

Martha was seven when her father became Governor of Virginia. She did not know how important an office this was, nor could she surmise Thomas Jefferson's unhappiness during his governorship. He was re-elected to a second term in 1780, and few governors ever took office in the face of greater discouragement. Though the masses were with him, the great land-owning families — among them many of his oldest, closest friends — were bitter over the changes he had introduced into the Virginia laws. Also, at last the British army had invaded Virginia, and every effort Governor Jefferson made to carry out George Washington's strategy met with failure.

Chapter III

GOOD-BY, MONTICELLO

BEFORE dawn on a certain spring morning in 1781, Martha woke with a start. Jane Carr, her cousin who shared the big fourposter bed, was sitting bolt upright, staring into the dark. Martha slid up on her pillow, wide awake, and touched her arm.

"What is it, Janie?" she whispered.

"Sh! Something's wrong, but I don't know what, Patsy. Someone came on horseback and I heard Uncle Tom say something. Then someone ran to the quarters. I reckon ——." She did not finish, for the door opened and Mrs. Carr, a shawl thrown over her nightgown, her face white in the wavering light of the candle she carried, hurried across the room.

"Quick, girls," she said, "get up! There's grave trouble. Jane, help Patsy with buttons, and do you both put on your heavy mantles and come down to the hall the moment you're dressed. But hurry!"

"But, Mamma," Jane's voice trembled in spite of herself, "what is it?"

"Naught to be alarmed about, dear, if we act quickly. A troop of British soldiers are on their way to *Monticello*. We must not be here when they come. Now hurry! The boys are up. Aunt Sukie's getting the babies ready. We haven't a moment to spare." She tossed the girls' stays and petticoats on the bed while she spoke, then lit their bedside candle from her own and hurried out, and they heard her swift steps along the hall.

For an instant Martha seemed frozen where she sat among the dishevelled bed-clothes. Then she flew into action. Nightcap ties jerked apart, stockings, stays, frilled drawers and ruffled petticoats settled into place. Jane, murmuring small, frightened observations, tugged at her own intricate clothes. Virginia Carr, twelve now and mature for her age, came in dressed and tucking her hair under a muslin cap. Little Mary Carr clung to her skirt, hopping up and down like an excited puppy while she explained, "We're goin' drivin' in the coach—Mamma and Auntie Jefferson and everybody. The boys are goin' to ride on their horses. Ginnie said so."

"Ready, darlings?" Virginia kept her voice steady while she pulled Jane's cape about her shoulders and, with her toe, swiftly retrieved one of Martha's slippers from under the bed.

Gratefully Martha stepped into it and blew out the candle. "We're ready," she said, and followed her cousins out through the unreal dusk.

In the great hall the family had gathered. Outside, the roomy coach and a phaeton stood waiting. Virginia had been mistaken; the boys would not ride their horses. Mrs. Carr and Mrs. Jefferson, Aunt Sukie, and the children would drive to a plantation fourteen miles away.

It was a silent little company that moved quickly across the gallery and into the waiting carriages. Only little Polly, drooping, half asleep over her nurse's shoulder, wept in bewildered indignation. Martha reached up to pat a little hand hanging limp against Aunt Sukie's arm.

"Hush, Sweet," she comforted. "We're all just going by-by together. Don't cry. We'll come back soon."

A hand was laid on her shoulder and Martha looked up to see her father smiling down at her. "My wise Patsy!" he said gravely. "Take care of Mamma and Little Sistah, and we'll all be together again in a few days, I promise."

She longed to ask questions but there was no time. In the coach she squeezed between Virginia and Jane and moved over to make room for Mary. The door snapped shut and the big coach rolled forward over the dew-drenched road.

Dabney Carr, the youngest of the boy cousins, sat between his mother and his Aunt Jefferson, facing the girls. Humiliation crimsoned his round cheeks and made his dark eyes darker. Fine how-de-do, stuffed in here with the women and children while Peter and Sam ride in the phaeton with Mr. Hutchins the overseer and Aunt Sukie! Baby stuff! Indignation made him reckless. His eyes met Martha's.

"Know what?" he blurted. "Know what happened, Patsy? I heard every word the man said when he came a-tearin' up on his horse, I did! He near fell off, too, and the horse heaved and blew something monstrous."

"What did he say, Dab?" Martha leaned forward eagerly.

Good-by, Monticello

"Dabney Carr, stop chattering like a magpie!" Mrs. Carr's voice was low and tense, but Dabney, having started, rushed on.

"He yelled, 'Mr. Jefferson! Mr. Jefferson! Tarleton's Raiders are coming to capture you if they can! You haven't a second to lose. Get away while there's time!' That's what he said, Pat, and a lot more. I heard him!"

Mrs. Jefferson sat with closed eyes, hearing neither the lad's excited chatter nor the rumbling of the coach. Her thoughts were back with the man alone at *Monticello*. Most of the night he had paced the gallery, worried, bewildered at the turn of events. Fortunate for him, though, that he had been there when the country boy, Jack Jouett, mounted on his wiry little mare, had galloped from Cuckoo Tavern in Louisa Court House Village to give the alarm. Would Thomas Jefferson escape? As Governor of Virginia and author of the Declaration of Independence, what chance would he have if captured?

Mrs. Jefferson bit her lip and suddenly her shoulders shook. Mrs. Carr put an arm around her and drew her heavy mantle closer.

Martha's teeth chattered partly from the damp, piercing cold of the spring dawn, and partly from sheer terror. Not until she was older would she know the entire story of this early morning escape; of how Jefferson, his family safe, had gone about collecting his most important papers, and of how he had just mounted his horse and galloped away when Captain McLeod and a troop of British dragoons had come swarming up the mountain.

Now she could only look helplessly from her mother to Dabney, angry at him for his boasting and at herself for having encouraged him in it. She leaned forward and softly touched her mother's knee. "Mamma, please don't— don't be sad," she begged, feeling very alone and wanting terribly to cry, yet knowing she must not. "Papa will be all right — he will, I make no doubt."

Outside, the gray mist-hung woods streamed by. There was no sound but the jingle of harness, the rumble of wheels and the measured, churning beat of horses' hoofs on the clay forest road.

The frightening spring and early summer days of 1781 were over. Thomas Jefferson's second term as Governor of Virginia, too, came to an end in June. In mid-October General Cornwallis surrendered at Yorktown and the Revolution was virtually ended. Before Christmas Martha made a polite farewell curtsy to the Baroness De Riedesel, and the family at *Monticello* settled down to a winter of quiet happiness.

Good-by, Monticello

In the spring another little sister, Lucy Elizabeth, came to share the nursery with Polly. Martha touched the round, satin-soft little cheek one morning as the baby lay across its mammy's lap. Polly, on tip-toe, eagerly reached up to investigate tiny, up-curled fingers.

"Sweetes' l'il lamb ever was," crooned Sukie, and Polly, enchanted, agreed. But Martha smiled down at dimpled, curly-headed Polly. Nowhere in the world was there as sweet a "l'il lamb" as "Little Sistah!"

Martha crossed the great hall to the door opening on the gallery where she thought she had heard her father's voice. In the doorway she stopped and caught her breath in surprise. Thomas Jefferson was deep in conversation with a stableboy who held a beautiful black pony by its halter while he passed his free hand over its shining withers and neck and slapped its broad chest in admiration. He grinned up at Martha, and her father turned and beckoned.

"How do you like her, Patsy?" he asked, smiling. "Time we rode together."

Martha went to stand beside the pony, her face a study. Here was the one thing she had been longing for ever since she first had watched the boys share their uncle's morning rides. Virginia Carr did not care for horses and their mother considered Jane and Mary too young to ride. Martha suspected her mother shared that opinion of her and had said

49

nothing. Now here was her dream come true. How had Papa guessed?

How, indeed? No father ever understood his child better than Thomas Jefferson understood his Patsy with her slow, half-grave, half-mischievous smile, her fiery temper, her hypersensitive nature that kept the color alternately flaming and fading across her high cheek bones. He knew her as well as he did his own high-spirited, rebellious nature.

So now father and daughter beamed at each other across the pony's cropped mane and Martha's soft-spoken "Oh, thank you, Papa!" was only an outward and audible sign of an inward and mutually understood pact of boundless devotion.

Nor was Martha's instruction in riding left to the clumsy if sincere efforts of a groom. A riding instructor arrived from Philadelphia within the week and by mid-summer nowhere in Virginia did a young girl ride with more grace or skill than did Miss Patsy Jefferson of *Monticello*, mounted on her little thoroughbred pony, Domino.

The early morning hours were the happiest of the day, for then Jefferson on his big hunter, Martha on her pony, would set out along the bridle path leading around the mountain and into the forest. From the earth's floor would rise the bitter-sweet scent of ancient, fallen, dew-soaked bark. Among the interlaced branches of oak and spruce

Good-by, Monticello

and feathery sycamore, bits of mist, like ghostly veils, twisted, fluttered and disappeared. Sometimes the two riders reined in their mounts to listen to the lovely morning song of a warbler or the gentle admonition of a mourning dove. Again, they stood upon a high plateau, looking out over the sleeping valley to the mountains beyond. *Monticello!* How they both loved it! How soon it would become for one a precious memory to be held high in her heart, a beacon across the years.

As the summer drew to a close, Martha, who was learning to sew and embroider under her mother's direction, found her lessons becoming shorter and shorter. Finally they stopped altogether. Once more a heavy silence hung over the mansion. Even Polly's merry laughter was muffled behind the closed nursery door. Martha, watching her father's stricken face as he came and went from her mother's room, remembered snatches of conversation over the sewing lessons: "Patience, daughter, patience and care in small things — this is important all through life. Try to remember, dear. No, take the stitch toward you, not away from you." The gentle voice, the deft, sure hands on the linen.... Martha's eyes filled and her chest ached with the sob that must be stifled.

It was at noon on a September day that Mrs. Carr sat down beside Martha on the top step of the west portico where, a small, dejected figure, she had huddled all morning in the hot sunshine.

"Patsy, dear," her aunt said gently, putting her hand over the small, tanned fingers clasped tightly in the little girl's lap, "you must be very brave now, and you must go to your father. He is in his room; he's asking for you."

With a terrible beating at her temples and throat and wrists, Martha got up and went into the silent house. As she crossed the great hall and turned toward the room which was her mother's, she heard a sound — soft, muffled, heartbreakingly sad.

Kneeling, with her head pressed against the door jamb of Mrs. Jefferson's room, was the Negro woman, Callie, who had been her maid. She was swaying slowly from side to side, and with every movement of her body, a primitive wailing, half croon, half moan, broke from her as if driven by some mechanical force: "Oh, God — Oh, Jesus — Oh, God. . . ." The sound echoed through the corridor, and now in the kitchen it was taken up by more voices until the air was filled with the eerie sound of keening.

For a moment Martha stood rooted to the spot, eyes wide, nostrils distended with the labored breathing that shook her whole body. Then she clapped her hands over her ears and ran to her father's room.

"Papa — Papa — Papa," she whispered as she ran.

Good-by, Monticello

Thus began the season of dreadful mourning for Thomas Jefferson when the ten-year-old Martha alone seemed to bring comfort. Together they walked or rode over the least frequented paths or through the unbroken forest of *Monticello*. As Martha herself wrote many years later: "In those melancholy rambles I was his constant companion — a solitary witness to many a burst of grief —."

Fortunately the new nation was again calling for his services. In November he received notice that Congress had appointed him to join Dr. Benjamin Franklin and Mr. John Adams in Europe, there to negotiate the peace treaty with England. Jefferson accepted the appointment. But now he was confronted with another problem. His little family must be separated. Quickly, almost sternly, he put natural sentiment aside. *Monticello* would be closed; the Carrs would move to one of the smaller family plantations; the six-months-old baby, Lucy Elizabeth and little Polly would go to their Aunt Elizabeth, Mrs. Eppes of *Eppington* on the James River.

Martha — ? What would be best for the child? He would be away for several years — send her with the Carr cousins whom she loved dearly? *Eppington,* on the other hand, was one of the show places along the James. Aunt Elizabeth was so very like Martha's own mother, her sister, and staying with her, especially as Polly too would be at

Eppington, would seem the perfect solution. Perfect, true, but not at all to the bereaved father's liking. Martha must go with him. For a moment, but only for a moment, Martha's jubilant happiness was unclouded.

The children at *Monticello* had been taught their sums, reading, and grammar by Mrs. Carr. Mrs. Jefferson, when her health permitted, taught them the rudiments of French and German. Thomas Jefferson himself had told them stories from English, French, and American History and insisted they read from the books of historical reference with which his library was so well stocked.

Within recent months Martha had heard her father speak again and again of the French Court, of young Lafayette and the monarch under whom he served, Louis XVI. The beautiful Queen, too, — what was her name? Marie Antoinette, yes, that was what Aunt Carr had called her and had added, " a beautiful and dangerously silly, heedless, young Queen." Now Papa was taking her, Martha, to France, so he said.

"Shall we see the Queen, Papa? And Versailles? And the new baby prince they call the Dauphin?" Martha asked, from the hassock where she sat beside her father in his study while he polished his violin, tightened its strings, tried its tone.

He looked at the grave, eager, young face turned up to

Good-by, Monticello

his and shook his head. "I very much doubt you will see the Court of France, daughter," he said. "Still, mayhap. Who knows? You will have much to write Polly about and much to tell her when we return."

"But, Papa, *isn't Little Sistah coming with us?*" Martha's voice was shrill and her eyes dark with incredulity.

Jefferson drew his thumb lightly along a string, tightening it, twanging it softly, then, "No, Patsy," he answered quietly. "Polly is little more than a baby. If she went with us a governess would have to be found and there is no time. The warship *Romulus* sails within the month. We must be in Baltimore before then. Winter travel is risky for a little one like Polly. Better far that she go to *Eppington* with Aunt Elizabeth." With this Martha had to be content though her eyes were stormy with the shock of her disappointment.

Quickly the days of preparation passed and at last, just before Christmas, Martha's father handed her into the coach that would carry them to Baltimore. *Monticello* was empty and silent. Winter lay white upon the land; trees, shrubs, flower beds were shrouded. Across the valley, even the mountains seemed to have receded. Martha leaned from the carriage window, one hand clutching her bonnet with its deep "poke," curls blowing in the wind.

"Good-by — Good-by — " she called, waving to a

55

little group of Negro children gathered beside the drive.

" 'By, Miss Patsy! 'By Mas' Tom!" they shouted, dancing in the biting air.

Then the coach rolled forward, down, down the mountain and, in her corner, Martha found herself whispering one word over and over, soundlessly, desperately. Only so could she keep from crying: *"Monticello — Monticello — Monticello."*

Chapter IV

THE BEST LAID PLANS

MARTHA lay in the big field bed staring into the dark. Outside, the soft May night was sweet with the scent of syringa and rain-wet grass. Thunder still rumbled distantly but the storm had passed and stars were beginning to wink against the velvety black of the sky.

The room where she lay was close for all its lavender and verbena-scented linen, its shining neatness, its gleaming mahogany. Mrs. Hopkinson, like all Colonial housewives, prided herself on her housekeeping, and her well-trained servants were constantly busy with endless expanses to be polished: silver, copper, brass, and pewter all to be kept in gleaming, spotless order.

Martha loved Mrs. Hopkinson, and the two years spent with her had, in the main, been happy ones. Thinking back over those two years made Martha suddenly restless. She sat up, threw back the covers, and slipped out of bed. She went to the window and softly, slowly, opened it. Hm, that was better. Warm, moist, fresh air poured into the room and she drew a chair to the window and tried to curl up in its stiff, unyielding mahogany depths. On an impulse she unfastened the starched ties of her nightcap and took it off and rested her head against the chair's hooped back.

So long, so terribly long ago it seemed since the blustery winter morning when she and her father had driven away from *Monticello*. When they had reached Baltimore it was bitter cold and, to Jefferson's dismay, the *Romulus* was held fast in the ice two miles off shore. Determined to reach the ship, the intrepid Virginian had his luggage loaded on a small boat, he and Martha got in, and they started, with twelve sturdy oarsmen battling the treacherous ice, to make their way out to the imprisoned ship.

Martha shuddered, remembering how their little craft had creaked and groaned as the jagged ice blocks had ground their sharp edges against it. Icy spray blew over them. She remembered her father's voice: "Keep your head down, Patsy!" She could still feel the sting of ice particles beating against her closed eyelids. Then, reluctantly, the order had been given to return to shore.

Tired out after the journey from Virginia and the attempted embarkation, Martha was not quite certain why or when her father had made the sudden decision to take her to Philadelphia and there place her in the care of Mrs. Hopkinson, mother of his friend Francis Hopkinson, the noted composer. She did, however, remember the evening of their arrival, and the glowing warmth of the Hopkinson drawing-room after the piercing cold of the coach that had brought the travelers from Baltimore.

Old Mrs. Hopkinson, plump and motherly and rustling faintly in her quilted petticoats and panniers, had put an arm about the tired girl and had led her upstairs.

Afterward, at dinner, Martha had met Francis Hopkinson, a tall, angular man about her father's age, in plum-colored breeches and waistcoat, fashionable white silk hose, and silver-buckled pumps. He had put her at her ease by grinning at her almost impishly as he helped himself a second time to Indian pudding. "You see, Miss Patsy," he said apologetically across a cloud of molasses-scented steam, "I need my strength to teach young ladies like you to play the harpsichord. It's no easy task for the most part, please believe me."

Martha knew he was teasing, and her own smile when she answered was just as merry. "I promise not to be too dull," she said. "Sometimes Papa and I play duets, he on his fiddle, I on the Forte-piano. I . . . ." At that point she remembered she was talking too much and stopped, blushing.

Across the table, Thomas Jefferson looked at his little daughter, at the candlelight touching her auburn curls, bringing out the soft gray-green in her eyes, the pink in her cheeks, and thought how proud her mother would have been.

Martha remembered the following morning when she parted from her father, he to return to Virginia on State and Government business, she to be entered as a day pupil in an exclusive Philadelphia school for girls on Pine Street.

For the first time in her life she found herself alone among strangers, charming gentlefolk, to be sure, but strangers nonetheless. Their ways were not the leisurely, easy-going ways of Virginia, their speech was hurried and clipped like the neat hedges around their tidy gardens. However, Martha would not have been Thomas Jefferson's daughter had she failed to adapt herself to new surroundings, and she succeeded admirably.

The Best Laid Plans

Mrs. Hopkinson heard her lessons and taught her to knit and to make some of the delicate lace-paper designs just coming into vogue. Martha, in turn, loved the plump, little, old lady and before spring had so far overcome her natural reserve and shyness as to tell her about her beloved *Monticello,* about "Little Sistah," and the Carr cousins. "Mistah Francis" became her champion. He was a strict but sympathetic teacher and under his tutelage Martha became a competent young musician. Francis Hopkinson was not only a noted musician and composer, but a poet and artist as well. His was the design of the thirteen stars representing the thirteen original states which was used for the first American flag. Nor was that all. With wealth and leisure to use as he chose, this aristocratic young Philadelphian for years gave his services as librarian in one of the first public libraries in America. He and Martha became fast friends.

Then there was Elisabeth. Elisabeth Trist was the classmate whom Martha singled out as her very special friend, and the two girls soon were inseparable.

Elisabeth was as short and round and dimpled as Martha was slender and tall. Perhaps her infectious laughter, her tireless delight in games — and this in a day when young ladies of ten, eleven and twelve were considered well beyond such childish folly — perhaps this all reminded Martha of Polly. Whatever the reason, the Trist and Jefferson families became the closest friends and many years later a daughter of Martha's married a son of the Trist family.

Together the girls worked over their sums and their drawing. Mr. and Mrs. Rittenhouse, friends of the Trists and the Hopkinsons, arranged to have them study drawing with a *Monsieur* Simitière, a French artist of high repute. Elisabeth frankly detested him. "He minces like a cockerel — so," she confided, giggling, and imitating the little man's affected gait so perfectly in spite of stays and hoops that Martha rocked in a gale of laughter.

Martha found his snuff-stained fingers and untidily pomaded hair unpleasant, still she berated herself for being so unappreciative when she realized how very much her father hoped *Monsieur* Simitière would consent to take her as a pupil. Thomas Jefferson wrote:

My dear Martha —

I am anxious to know what books you read, what tunes you play, and to receive specimens of your drawing. With respect to your meeting M. Simitière at Mr. Rittenhouse's nothing could give me more pleasure than your being much with that worthy family, wherein you will see the best examples of rational life, and learn to esteem and copy them. But I should be very tender of intruding you on the family; as it might, perhaps, be not always convenient for you to be there at your hours of attending M. Simitière. I can only say, then, that if it has been desired by Mr. and Mrs. Rittenhouse, in such a manner as that Mrs. Hopkinson shall be satisfied that they will not think it inconvenient, I would have you thankfully accept it; and conduct yourself with so much attention to the family as that they may never feel themselves incommoded by it. I hope Mrs. Hopkinson will be so good as to act for you in this matter with that delicacy and prudence of which she is so capable. I have much at heart your learning to draw, and should be uneasy at your losing this opportunity, which probably is your last.

Martha re-folded the letter in an unhappy frame of mind. True, she had not wanted the lessons with *Monsieur* Simitière and had been delighted when the pompous little man had announced he was returning to France. Now Papa would be disappointed. It was hard to know when you were wishing wisely, Martha reflected.

Meanwhile, the father she loved so dearly was having a perplexing time. The peace treaty which he had expected to help Dr. Franklin and Mr. Adams negotiate in Europe, had been signed. However, he had been re-elected to Congress which now met at Annapolis. Many important matters were being decided by that Congress and the fine mind, the clear judgment of Thomas Jefferson were needed to help settle them. One of these was the question of American coinage. It was Thomas Jefferson who suggested (and the Congress adopted) the dollars-and-cents coinage system which we use today. These were some of the beloved father's occupations while, in Philadelphia, his daughter was learning to play "Lady Coventry's Minuet" on the harpsichord and to conjugate French verbs.

So the two years passed and on a May morning in 1784 Martha had a letter that sent her flying to Mrs. Hopkinson. The old lady looked up from her embroidery frame as Martha, in the doorway, made a swift curtsy and hurried across the morning room.

"Methinks we have good news, eh, child?" she queried, a gentle smile lighting her face.

"Oh, yes, Mrs. Hopkinson. Papa's coming for me! We're . . . we're going to France after all!" The letter crackled in Martha's fingers and she smoothed it to read what was written. "He says . . . here it is . . . he has been chosen by the Congress to help Dr. Franklin and Mr. Adams with trade treaties. He'll be here, he says, May 17th . . . that's but a fortnight . . . and he's sending down to *Monticello* for Callie to go with us, to be my maid.

Patsy Jefferson of Monticello

She was Mamma's, you know. Oh, Mrs. Hopkinson, is it unseemly to be so excited? I'm fair out of my wits!'' Frock of delicate ivory-and-rose cashmere forgotten, Martha dropped to her knees and buried her face in Mrs. Hopkinson's lap.

The old lady's dark eyes were suspiciously bright behind her spectacles as she patted the bowed head. ''This house will seem empty without you, sweet maid,'' she said softly.

Martha stirred. Tomorrow! In only a few hours it would be here, the eagerly awaited day, May 17th. Her trunks, packed and locked, stood in the hall. In her portmanteau, on top where she could reach it quickly, was the purse she had knitted for her father. He would use it on the journey.

She got up, yawned and stretched. To France with Papa, *anywhere* with Papa, would be adventure to rouse envy in anyone. Even Elisabeth had admitted: ''Mm, Patsy Jefferson, but I do envy you! Off to Europe just like a Miss Somebody from Somewhere, and with your papa such an important person I doubt not you'll come back spoiled something outrageous.'' Then she had all but crushed Martha in a hug to take out the sting in the words.

The Best Laid Plans

Martha smiled in the dark. How wonderful if we were going back to *Monticello,* she thought.

Far down Third Street she could hear the receding voice of the town crier: "Two o'clock and all's well." Softly she closed the window and climbed back into bed.

Chapter V

TWO ON A JOURNEY

ELISABETH danced about in a very fever of excitement.
She had been permitted to come to the Third Street house
to tell her friend good-by, and now that the moment of
parting actually had arrived, tears and dimples chased one
another across her round cheeks.

"You'll see the Queen of France, Patsy," she crowed,
"think of it — the beautiful, sinful Queen of France! 'Tis

Two On a Journey

said her Palace at Versailles is lined, mind you, Patsy, *lined* with gold and diamonds while the people of France starve!"

Martha smoothed the lacquered top of her new hat box with pictures of trees and fountains painted on it, and smiled across its shining cover at Elisabeth. The two girls were sitting in a corner of the drawing-room, while outside, Thomas Jefferson and Francis Hopkinson were superintending the loading of Martha's bags on the luggage cart. In the doorway leading to the hall, the woman Callie smilingly stood guard beside a mound of hand luggage and heavy wraps.

"I'll probably not see the Queen, Betsy," Martha answered. "Papa most likely will be at the Palace sometimes on business but I doubt I'll ever see Versailles. Mrs. Hopkinson says she's sure Marie Antoinette is not sinful— only heedless and extravagant. I'd love to see her, though. She sounds so beautiful — golden hair, blue eyes. . . ."

"Ready, Patsy?" Thomas Jefferson came in, followed by the Hopkinsons. Little Mrs. Hopkinson, leaning on her son's arm, was flushed and trembling. Martha had filled the place of a granddaughter during the two years with her, and the parting proved to the old lady how deep had become her affection for the soft-spoken, auburn-haired girl from Virginia.

But soon the adieus were over and Martha, seated beside

her father in the high phaeton, was tucking the fine muslin duster around her and settling back to enjoy her drive. The pair of handsome sorrels were pawing the ground and tossing their heads, impatient to be off, testing the strength and patience of the servant who held them. Jefferson drew on his gloves, gathered up the reins, and, with a last quick gesture of farewell to the group waving from the stoop, drove off into the May morning.

Bit chains rattled smartly, sunlight flashed on the polished wheel spokes as the stylish phaeton rolled along Third Street, followed by its equally neat and well-appointed luggage cart. The Jeffersons would drive to Trenton, there to change to coach. Not until the Hopkinson dwelling was many blocks behind did Martha cease to hear Elisabeth's half tearful, half laughing, "'By Patsy— 'by Patsy — 'by. . . ."

The weeks that followed were like a panorama picture book to Martha. The only journey she ever had taken was the hurried one from *Monticello* to Baltimore, to Philadelphia, Now, first by carriage, then by coach or river boat, she was traversing one state after another — New Jersey, New York, Connecticut, Massachusetts.

There was much Thomas Jefferson wanted to learn at first hand about American commerce before he discussed it with representatives of European countries. Time was

70

short; mail was slow. He would go himself. He would talk to farmers, ship builders, manufacturers of leather goods, brass, and other things in which American men were beginning to take justifiable pride. Only so, he believed, would he get a clear understanding of his country's business; of what it had to offer other countries; of its needs and hopes from those countries in return.

Without hurrying, yet traveling briskly, using the hours carefully, he could accomplish this and still be in Boston in ample time to embark on the good ship *Ceres* on July 5th.

To Martha it was a time of pure enchantment. The weather was perfect. Spring poured its golden warmth lavishly over the land, birds sang in the hedges, and beside her was the father she loved with every fiber of her intense, sensitive nature.

And Jefferson, to his deep satisfaction, was discovering how much the two years in Philadelphia had done for his Patsy. For she was a new Patsy, eager to tell him about school days, asking leading, intelligent questions about his own plans and problems. The rather quiet, grave little girl had given place to a gay, charming young companion whose lively chatter again and again set her father laughing heartily.

New York both amazed and disappointed Martha.

Patsy Jefferson of Monticello

Somehow, she had expected something more stately and shining, a city with water pumps at intervals along its best streets as in Philadelphia. Here there were only wells at every fourth street crossing, and the water not too appetizing. Pigs wallowed in the dirty streets, and Martha stepped daintily, holding up her skirts — and her nose — as she hurried along beside her father.

However, there was much in the city that she loved. One thing of which she never could get enough was driving on the Broadway in an open carriage. The north end of the Broadway was the fashionable driveway of the city. Here, in the late afternoon, one saw many beautifully gowned women flashing by in their open carriages, many dashing horsemen cantering along in the spring sunshine.

Thomas Jefferson engaged a handsome carriage and team for his use while in New York, and almost every afternoon found the two companions enjoying their drive up the broad Avenue and out into the open country, which is Central Park today.

Jefferson's striking, somewhat austere appearance was familiar to practically everyone, and he was hard pressed keeping a firm hand on his mettlesome team and at the same time doffing his hat to acknowledge the continuous greetings of passersby.

Martha beamed with happiness and pride at the homage

paid him and time and time and again broke into snatches of song as their carriage whirled over the sun-warmed pavement.

The days lengthened into weeks; New York was left behind. Martha in later years remembered certain taverns where stops were made to change coaches or to spend the night: Williams Inn beside a blue lake on the King's Highway near Marlboro; Pequod Inn at Sudbury; the tavern at Norwalk where brave townsfolk were re-building their lovely little city destroyed by the British five years earlier. And then the travelers were in Boston, with only two days remaining before they sailed for England — and France.

Callie unpacked, laundered rumpled linens in the inn's vast kitchen; mended bonnet ribbons, and shampooed Martha's hair. Jefferson visited fisheries, discussed salt fish and whale-oil export. Then he was off to the Leonard Iron Works, sixteen miles out from the city, and returned with his note books filled.

Martha had a new green bonnet to match the pretty frock of dark green silk which Mrs. Trist had had made for her in Philadelphia. On the last afternoon of their stay in Boston Jefferson lifted the bonnet from its box and handed it to Martha, smiling broadly.

"We're paying a farewell call, Patsy," he said, "and I want you to look your prettiest."

Patsy Jefferson of Monticello

"Call, Papa?" Martha gave the knitting with which she had been struggling to Callie and looked up eagerly. Her fingers were moist; the stocking yarn prickled uncomfortably in the July heat.

"H'm, yes. We're going to visit someone you've heard me speak of often — Mr. Revere."

"*Paul Revere,* Papa?" Martha was on her feet now. "Callie, I'll wash my hands, please, — just a little water in the basin — oh, Papa, how wonderful! I'd no notion he lived here in Boston. I should have known of course." She busied herself turning up the tight cuffs of her dress while Callie poured water into the wash bowl.

"You were a mite of three when he and Will Dawes took their patriotic ride, but one day, I make no doubt, the name of Paul Revere will be remembered, and meeting the man himself will be something to tell your grandchildren about. So on with your bonnet. His shop is on the other side of town and we have a long walk."

Martha cooled her hot face and hands and smoothed her hair and tied the green bonnet strings under her chin. "Don't fret, Callie," she counseled, sensing the colored woman's dread at being left alone in the strange room. "Mayhap you'd turn the heel in the sock for me, and by that time we'll be back." She patted the broad shoulder and followed her father out of the room.

Two On a Journey

Down Summer Street, across Short and into Essex they went, keeping whenever possible, in the shade.

"But, I thought Paul Revere was a silversmith, Papa," Martha whispered as they entered the pleasant, spacious shop.

Her father did not at once answer — possibly he did not hear. He was threading his way between counters on which were arranged hardware of excellent quality: ornamental door knockers and hinges; wall sconces of bronze, brass, or pewter; sheets (not rolls) of beautifully designed wall paper; bolts of fine cloth, and even packages of stationery. True, one section of the shop was given over to silverware, and here Martha noticed a man bending over a table, laboriously polishing a small object which now and then he held from him, squinting at it, appraising its luster.

Thomas Jefferson had approached so quietly that the man did not realize he had visitors until a shadow fell across his polishing. Then:

"Ah, good-day, Sir. Why . . . why. . . ." The cloth dropped from his fingers, his broad, ruddy face flushed crimson, and a smile of welcome and delighted surprise spread across it as he held out his hand. "Why, it's Mr. Jefferson . . . *Mr. Thomas Jefferson*," he stammered, coming out from behind the desk. "Welcome . . . welcome to Boston!"

Patsy Jefferson of Monticello

Jefferson grasped the proffered hand cordially and presented Martha who found herself wondering how so stockily built a man could have ridden a horse at the breakneck speed with which Paul Revere had covered the miles to Lexington on that spring night in 1775. She liked him instantly and, when his firm craftsman's fingers closed over her small hand, she spoke with a gracious warmth so like her mother's that Jefferson caught his breath.

"Papa said we were paying a farewell call on someone he'd often told me of," she said, smiling up at him from under her green bonnet. "I am so very glad he did, Mr. Revere . . . I am, indeed."

And Paul Revere, marveling at the poise and charm of the Southern girl, reminded himself to mention it that very evening to his own fourteen-year-old Elizabeth.

Martha would have spent the afternoon happily in Paul Revere's cool, spacious shop that smelled so pleasantly of beeswax and pencils and coating cloth. But there was still some packing to do, and they must be up betimes in the morning. Thomas Jefferson bought fiddle strings, and an inkhorn, and helped Martha select a pad of writing paper. Then they stepped back into the glare of the summer day and began their long walk to the inn.

Chapter VI

VARIABLE WINDS

MARTHA enjoyed every moment of the nineteen days aboard the *Ceres*. The ship, so new and spic and span and shining, had many conveniences heretofore unknown on shipboard. Narrower than most ships of that day, she cut the waves with the grace and speed of a bird, her snowy sails straining before a steady wind.

78

Variable Winds

There were only six passengers aboard including Colonel Tracy, her owner; food was plentiful and delicious, and as though to provide entertainment for the notable company, whales were sighted again and again, and those strange, blue, balloon-like fish called Portuguese men-of-war, occasionally rode the waves close by, trailing their rope-like tentacles behind them.

Time passed quickly and on the evening of July 24th the *Ceres* landed her passengers at Cowes on the Isle of Wight on the southern coast of England. Now the sky was overcast. The sun set in a bank of black clouds, casting eerie green shadows over the English Channel, and thunder muttered far inland. Standing between her father and Callie on the wharf, watching while the last of their luggage was loaded on the little channel boat which would carry them to France, Martha bit her lip nervously.

In the harbor the water was calm enough, but out in the channel waves were running high, with plumes of white spray flying from their crests.

"A bad night, Mr. Jefferson," observed the skipper, hurrying up the narrow gangplank. "If you'll come aboard now, please, we'll make for the open channel while yet a spot of light is left."

Martha followed her father down into the small, close cabin, Callie hovering at her heels; and a glance from a porthole showed the pilings of the wharf sliding by. They were moving out toward the channel. A sudden gust of wind that brought rain lashing against the walls, went whistling shrilly away into the dusk, making the little boat pitch sharply. Two lighted whale-oil lamps on the wall gave off a rancid, sickly odor. Above the roar of the sea, the whistling wind and the creaking of the boat, came the continuous crash of thunder; lightning whipped and twisted around the plunging craft like a lariat in the hands of evil genii.

Martha, determined to be a good sailor to the end of the journey, tried first standing, looking from the porthole, then sitting decorously beside her father on the bench which circled the cabin walls. Finally, however, white and trembling, she crumpled in Callie's outstretched arms. And Callie, her eyes big with terror, put her own fears and discomforts behind her and held her beloved "Miss Patsy" close, whispering encouragement.

So morning came at last, and the weary travelers disembarked at Havre. At a little water-front tavern Martha dashed cold water on her grimy, sweat-streaked face and turned dutifully while Callie brushed her skirts and straightened her fichu. Jefferson, his face lined with fatigue, looked at her with pride.

"You're a good traveler, my Pat," he said fondly. "That

was a wretched channel trip. And you, Callie," turning to the woman who was busying herself with the hand luggage, "Miss Patsy couldn't have done without you. When we reach Paris buy yourself a pretty with this." He placed a generous coin in her hand and Callie curtsied her thanks, beaming. Mas' Tom understood folks' hearts; there was no kinder master on top o' earth.

Five days later the Jefferson coach and luggage van rumbled into Paris and drew up before the Hotel d'Orleans in the rue des Petits Augustins. Heads turned and dark eyes gazed in friendly appraisement as the distinguished-looking American and his slender, auburn-haired daughter and white-turbaned servant alighted and entered the hotel.

"Regarde donc! Voilà Monsieur Thomas Jeff-air-son, l'Américan le plus distingué!" they whispered to one another. *"Tiens, et regarde l'Africaine! Est-ce que c'est une doméstique, crois tu? Que la jeune fille est gentille!"*

Martha could scarcely believe her ears. Actually she was understanding French! She had studied the language at school and Mr. Hopkinson had coached her tirelessly. Now she could understand!

"Methinks you're going to outdo me where this language is concerned, Patsy," laughed her father in their sitting room that evening. "Albermarle County's in every word I utter while you give the words a much. neater twist, a more Parisian flavor. Mark me, you'll return to Virginia speaking French like any French girl. Which reminds me. . . ."

Martha had been selecting a quill from the desk drawer to write a letter to Elisabeth Trist — there was so much to write. Now she looked up. "Yes, Papa?"

"You recall our talks aboard ship about a school, Patsy?"

Yes, Martha recalled them, and for a moment a frown creased her brows. Then she laughed ruefully and came to stand beside her father, her arm across his shoulder. "Mm, I do remember," she answered.

He smiled up at her, one eyebrow quirked quizzically, and she continued a little shamefacedly: "I hoped — that is, I think I hoped we wouldn't bother with school as long as I spoke French. I thought perhaps I could have lessons with you, Papa. It would be so — so much more — oh, pleasant, somehow."

Jefferson drew her to him. "Aye, my Patsy, more pleasant it would be, no doubt," he answered, thinking how many pleasant plans and hopes in his little family circle had had to bow before necessity. "But you see, dear, my duties here will keep me very busy and besides, you should be with young people. I explained to you that I'd written to a friend here in Paris about a French school — you remember?"

Martha nodded.

"Well, when we arrived this afternoon I found a letter from the Marquise de Lafayette waiting for me. She has made all arrangements for you to enter the—here it is—." He fumbled in his pocket and brought out the Marquise's letter with its ribbon and enormous seal, and opened it. "It is called — hm — here — *L'Abbaye Royale de Pan-thémont.*"

"A convent, Papa? *With nuns?*" Martha's voice was a mere whisper, her eyes were very dark and shining. "One of the girls at school in Philadelphia had an aunt who was a nun!"

"Really? Well, judging from the Marquise's letter, the ladies in charge at *Panthémont* are exactly the sort I should want you to study under. It is almost impossible to be admitted there as a pupil unless one is of noble family. So I am doubly grateful to the Lafayettes for using their influence in persuading the sisters to make a place for my Patsy from Virginia."

Martha still was not sure that she liked the idea. Somehow she had dreamed of her life in France as being spent almost entirely with her father and his friends. On shipboard the mention of school had been vaguely disturbing but she had pushed the thought from her. Now here it was again and this time a concrete fact. She was going to a convent. Two thoughts struck her simultaneously and with almost equal force.

"When am I going? What will Callie do?" she demanded a little breathlessly and slipped to a hassock beside her father's chair. The sudden prospect of a new parting had made her knees unsteady.

"I can answer your last question first, Patsy," he answered. "I have taken a house not far from here; I shall — rather *we* shall probably move in in a day or so. Callie shall care for my linen — keep it mended and properly sorted. You remember how she did it at *Monticello?* And now and then when mayhap we're both a little hungry for Virginia cooking, I'll send for you and Callie shall make us a dinner of ham and greens cooked in pot liquor, with corn bread. Sound good?"

Jefferson smiled down at Martha as the picture shaped in his mind and she smiled back, nodding, biting her lip to stop its sudden quivering.

Her father saw and patted her hand. "As to when you enter school, dear, that will depend. You will need a new wardrobe, and there will be many things to be attended to before you go. And after all, you know it isn't as though you were to leave Paris. The convent is right here in the city and we'll be seeing each other often."

"And perhaps Little Sistah will be coming over, too, won't she?"

"Yes, possibly in the spring. Now. . . ." The conversation had taken on a dangerously homesick tone and the father cast about for something to dispel the gloom.

On the table lay his violin case. He crossed the room, opened the case and took out the graceful instrument. He tucked it under his chin and slowly drew the bow across it. Then a jig, so merry, so compelling, rollicked across the strings that, in spite of herself, Martha laughed aloud and began clapping. Softly the door leading to her room opened and Callie stood there, beaming. Unconsciously, automatically her old palms began beating time.

"Seem like we's back home, don't it, Miss Patsy?" she laughed, turbaned head bobbing.

"Hmhm," Martha nodded agreement, not breaking the rhythm of her clapping.

"This is home, too," she added softly — almost to herself, and thought suddenly as she said it, *Wherever* we are is home if we think so.

The history of *L'Abbaye Royale de Panthémont*, Martha decided as she listened to the dark-eyed little Marquise de Lafayette describe it, made her think of a piece of very old, very beautiful tapestry. Humility, courage, faith, and

85

selfless pride were the threads which through centuries had kept its design clear, its fabric strong.

Founded by the Bernardine Sisters in Panthémont in the diocese of Beauvaise in 1217, it was long a center of Medieval culture. Within its bleak walls many a little duchess learned the lessons of gentle deportment and humility while weaving a length of cloth-of-gold for her dower chest; many a young noblewoman forsook the dissolute Court life of the 13th and 14th Centuries for a life of contemplation and good works. Years passed and then in the 17th Century the River Avelon flooded the countryside and the ancient convent crumbled in the rushing waters. In spite of terror and loss of life, the courageous sisters refused long to be discouraged. In 1672 they bought the Augustine Convent of the Incarnate Word in Paris and re-named it *L'Abbaye Royale de Notre Dame de Panthémont*. Later this was shortened to *L'Abbaye Royale de Panthémont* or simply to *Panthémont*.

As always in the past, to *Panthémont* came daughters of royal and noble families. It was the most fashionable boarding school in France if not, indeed, in all Europe.

Martha listened eagerly while the Marquise described various nuns she herself had known there as a girl, gentlewomen who passed on to their young charges unforgettable, lofty standards of life.

Variable Winds

Now, seated beside her father in the carriage as it traversed the *Faubourg Saint Germain,* Martha was very quiet. For one thing, she was uncomfortable. The Marquise had taken her to a fashionable hairdresser and her curls had been frizzed and brushed high into a pompadour and then permitted to fall in clusters on her shoulders. A large hat of heavy blue silk towered over this elaborate headdress and effectually shut out what little air found its way into the carriage.

Martha's slim young body was rendered slimmer still by new, long, heavily boned stays and, with no regard for the August heat wave which was sweeping Paris, she was wearing the dress uniform prescribed by the convent: a frock of ribbed, watered, crimson silk, with wide, stiffly starched cuffs and collar. It fell in heavy, graceful folds over supporting hoops and petticoats, leaving its wearer a small, wilted mortal, lost in its depths.

As the carriage swung into the *rue de Bellechasse* and the high wall of the convent came into view, Jefferson put his hand over Martha's in its correct linen glove.

" 'Twill be interesting, Patsy," he said, guessing the misgiving she felt. "Remember, dear, at home we would call this 'the sickly season' — August. 'Twill not always be so uncomfortably warm. And tomorrow I'll drive over to see you."

Martha nodded and smiled, not trusting her voice to answer, and smoothed the blue silk bag which contained her handkerchief and purse. The carriage slowed and stopped. The footman opened the door, set Martha's bags on the pavement and stood aside as her father alighted and handed her out.

She crossed a narrow sward in the shade of great plane trees and saw before her an enormous door of carved, dark wood set in a high stone wall which stretched in both directions as far as her eyes could follow.

Thomas Jefferson lifted the heavy knocker, and a moment after it fell, a grill high in the door opened and Martha caught a quick glimpse of a face. Then the door swung open.

Often and often during the four years she spent at *Pan-thémont* Martha tried to re-capture the first impression she had as she entered the convent grounds under the stone arch of the wall on that stifling August afternoon in 1784. It was an impression of green coolness; of swaying branches and the golden shower of twin fountains; of bricked paths winding to vine-hung arbors or across wide stretches of lawn, to lose themselves in more distant alleys of laurel and arbor vitæ. This was a picture Martha never forgot.

Beside her moved a sister in the blue habit of the Bernardine order whose voice was full of soft laughter, whose delicate features and every movement bespoke gentle breeding. They entered the convent building and here, in the *salon,* the Jeffersons were presented to *Madame l'Abbesse,* a tall, imperious looking woman whose rather haughty expression thawed a little under Thomas Jefferson's courtly greeting. She took Martha's warm hand in its rumpled linen glove in her cool, firm grasp and smilingly addressed her in French.

"Welcome to *Panthémont,* my child," she said. "You will be happy here with us, I am sure. The other girls know you are coming and are eager to welcome you. I regret," she turned to Jefferson, "that I cannot invite *Monsieur* to inspect our dormitories and *petits salons;* they are for the members of the *Panthémont* household only. *Mademoiselle Marthe* will want to refresh herself now, so perhaps *Monsieur* will excuse us?"

So quietly, withal so graciously it was done that Martha realized afterward she had felt no wrench at parting. After the deep curtsy to the Abbess in which she had been instructed by the Marquise, and a correct, *"Au revoir,* Papa," she followed another *religieuse* into a cool, vaulted, stone corridor and up a circular flight of stone steps, then another long passage and a sudden turn into a small room.

"See, *Mademoiselle!"* The nun motioned her to the single window and pointed below. Martha stood beside her,

and as she looked, a warm glow of happiness welled in her heart. In a shady alley surrounded by a high, clipped hedge, a group of girls about her own age were playing croquet, their occasional exclamations and laughter mingling with the constant clack — clack — clack of mallet on ball. In a far corner of the alley, a nun sat reading aloud to a class of kindergarteners who formed a semicircle on the grass facing her. Something in the story amused them and they rocked in mirth, their high, clear laughter tinkling like wind bells.

Martha turned to the nun beside her. "It is like an ancient garden in a story book, Sister," she said softly. "It doesn't seem at all a part of a big city like Paris, does it?"

"Well, now, as to that I cannot say," laughed her companion. "We are all so used to our dear *Panthémont* that I think we are a little blind to some of its beauty. Perhaps you would like to change to the thinner school uniform and then I will introduce you to the other *jeunes filles*. And," she added as an afterthought as she turned away, "here we say '*Madame*' instead of 'Sister.' I am *Madame* de Taubenheim." She smiled her sunny smile again and then Martha heard the diminishing rustle of her habit and the whisper of her rosary beads as she hurried away down the corridor.

Martha turned and looked about her little room. The walls were gray; the narrow bed immaculate white. Patterned sunlight played across the table on which stood a candlestick and snuffer; across a rush-bottomed chair, a high chest of drawers. That was all. She stood very still. From far away came the rumble and roar of Paris. Here within these ancient walls were serenity and peace, a green oasis. She heard the soft splash of fountains and from somewhere nearby caught the sound of voices chanting the *Nunc Dimitis*. Martha turned again to the window. The croquet players were gone. The garden was empty. Resolutely she took off her bonnet and began unfastening her collar.

Chapter VII

MADEMOISELLE JEFFY

AUTUMN rains transformed the boulevards of Paris into
shining mirrors and the convent gardens into a brown,
sodden mass.

Indoors, Martha studied French literature and history
of art with *Madame* de Taubenheim and music under the
great organist, Claude Balbastre. She liked the girls and
they liked her. They began by calling her *"Mademoiselle
Jeff-air-son,"* swung to *"Patsee Jeff-air-son"* and finally,

93

with an affectionately eloquent shrug, settled on "Jeffy."
So "Jeffy" she remained during the next four years.

They were strange years, years with a dream-like quality, A fourteen-year-old duchess of the House of Lorraine
taught her a trick of matching thread for her embroidery;
her favorite croquet opponent was a ruddy-cheeked, black-
haired little Bourbon princess; the only serious quarrel she
had was with yet another princess of the blood.

"*Tiens,* Jeffy," the princess sneered, "you Americans
are very amusing. You think you are such free people. You
talk all the time of liberty — liberty — liberty. *Mon Dieu,*
you act as though no other nation knew its meaning! Yet,
with all your precious 'liberty' you have slavery. Here in
la belle France, we think that is disgraceful. You should be
ashamed!"

To her astonishment and dismay she found she had chal-
lenged a girl whose poise far surpassed her own.

Martha, who was tall for her age and bore herself with
admirable dignity, looked coolly down her aristocratic nose.
"You, not I, began this discussion, Your Highness," she
said slowly. "I am no more responsible for a regrettable law
of my country than you are for some of the regrettable laws
of your own. I am a guest in your country, furthermore,
so it is you and not I who should be ashamed."

Martha's triumph was short-lived however, for *Madame*

Mademoiselle Jeffy

l'Abbesse demanded that both girls apologize — which they did somewhat sheepishly — and were better friends thereafter.

Twice a week Martha was permitted to visit her father and frequently several of the girls went with her, and Jefferson would find himself host to a group of chattering, giggling French *demoiselles* who, for all their manners and graces, ate with the appetites of Virginia field hands the delicious fried chicken and cream cakes Callie set before them.

Thomas Jefferson had taken a villa outside the city proper, on a highway leading to the Royal Palace at Versailles. It was a handsome establishment befitting his position as American Minister, and no more distinguished gatherings were to be found anywhere in Paris than at the American Embassy.

Jefferson's courtly manners and diplomacy made him vast numbers of friends but to very few of them did he permit so much as a glimpse behind the scenes of the sparkling drama of his public life. Behind the scenes there was little of sparkle, much of deep anxiety and sorrow.

Shortly after the New Year in 1785 a letter from Eppington, Virginia, written three months earlier, brought word of the death of baby Lucy Elizabeth in October. Jefferson was stunned, and Martha, looking from his stricken face to the open letter in his hand, could think of only one thing to say: "We must send for Polly *tout de suite,* Papa. We three must be together!" And Jefferson pressed her hand and nodded, tight lipped. Aye, they must be together.

So began a long series of letters to and from the Eppes family. Polly adored her Aunt Eppes and the prospect of going to France held little attraction for her. Answering her father's affectionate invitations, the little girl wrote frankly:

Dear Papa — I long to see you, and hope that you and sister Patsy are well; give my love to her and tell her that I long to see her, and hope that you and she will come very soon to see us. I hope that you will send me a doll. I am very sorry that you have sent for me. I don't want to go to France, I had rather stay with Aunt Eppes. Aunt Carr, Aunt Nancy and Cousin Polly Carr are here. Your most happy and dutiful daughter. Polly Jefferson.

The father smiled and shook his head. Another letter began its long journey across the ocean; another, and still another. It was not until two years later that "Aunt Eppes" hit upon a scheme to get headstrong little Polly started on her way to France. It took courage and certainly it required cooperation of the most exacting kind.

Captain Ramsay's ship lay in the James River just above

Mademoiselle Jeffy

Eppington, and every day for a week the children from the Eppes household were taken aboard to play on the sunny main deck. Polly became an instant favorite with bluff, kindly Captain Ramsay and soon counted the early hours of each day as so much time lost until she could go racing up the gangplank, curls flying, shouting "Ahoy! Here I come! Ahoy, Captain Ramsay!"

A Negro woman, Isabell Heming, always accompanied the children. One day they failed to notice that Mrs. Eppes kissed Polly with more tenderness than usual as she waved them off, or that Isabell was carrying a cloak over her arm. They romped as usual, and separated for afternoon naps. When Polly awoke a few hours later and ran out on deck, calling the other children, only the Captain and the smiling Isabell met her. The Virginia shore line was moving slowly by. They were sailing toward England.

Meanwhile, in France, Thomas Jefferson was sorely disturbed over the unrest in the country he loved second only to the United States.

Louis XVI was a dull-witted, easygoing monarch, dominated by his gay, irresponsible wife, Marie Antoinette. While she poured millions of francs into the building of artificial brooks and waterfalls and played at being milk-maid — with pails of crested silver — in her beautiful little make-believe hamlet within the park at Versailles, the poor people of France lived in desperate want. In writing about it to a friend, Jefferson said, "Of twenty millions of people supposed to be in France, I am of the opinion that there are nineteen millions more wretched, more accursed in every circumstance of human existence than the most conspicuously wretched individual of the whole United States."

Like the distant thunder of a slowly approaching summer storm, the first faint roll of the terrible drums of revolution could be heard by any who chose to listen. And Thomas Jefferson, the successful American Revolution still so close to his heart, so fresh in his memory, listened and was dismayed.

Unlike the Americans, the French lacked calm logic and discernment. Emotion, fiery and unpredictable as forked lightning, was rampant in most of the discussions to which Jefferson listened. Also, France lacked leaders of stability. Lafayette, himself in wholehearted sympathy with the people, admitted this. France, beautiful, warmhearted France! What was in store for her?

At *Panthémont,* Martha too, heard the muffled rattle of drums, though here only very faintly. Behind their unfailing cheerfulness, the sisters were uneasy, and some of the girls whose parents were closely associated with the

Royal household, looked suddenly grave and old beyond their years. Martha was working hard with her music and by the end of her second year under *Monsieur* Balbastre's tutelage she had become quite a finished musician. Her greatest delight was accompanying her father when he played his violin. Jefferson had bought from a man named John Randolph some years earlier a rare violin, a Cremona, made in 1660 by the noted violin maker, Nicholaus Amati. He always had played the violin with marked skill and now he took especial pride in playing his fine instrument for the entertainment of his friends, with Martha playing the accompaniment on the harpsichord.

Sunday afternoon at the American Embassy was the brightest spot in Martha's week. She was almost fifteen now, the age at which Marie Antoinette had become the bride of Louis XVI, and was thoroughly enjoying meeting the brilliant company gathered under her father's hospitable roof. The Lafayettes; the Duchess de la Rochefoucauld d'Auville; Johann Krumpholtz, the noted harpist and friend of Francis Hopkinson of Philadelphia; the Duchess of Kingston with her amusing lisp; the noted beauty, Mrs. Cosway, who instantly won Martha's heart by calling her "Patsy;" these were a few of the people Martha met in her father's *salon* on the *rue de Berri* on the road to Versailles.

Patsy Jefferson of Monticello

One Autumn Sunday afternoon she stepped from her carriage, followed by a maid, and ran up the steps of the Embassy. Her cheeks were flushed, her lips smiling in anticipation of the delightful evening ahead. She nodded a pleasant greeting to the lackey at the door, handed shawl and gloves to the maid and caught the eye of the *maître d'hôtel* who announced her.

Judging from the babble of voices pouring from the *salon* as the door was opened, Martha suspected a large company had already gathered. Her suspicions were justified. The great oval *salon,* its gilt and rose rococo paneling already a-twinkle with early candlelight, was crowded with ladies in towering hair dresses and billowing satin and brocades, and with gentlemen in powdered wigs, lace ruffs and shimmering satin smallclothes. The air was heavy with the scent of musk and verbena and spiced rose petals.

Martha threaded her way among them, greeting this group, stopping to chat for a moment with that, happy in the knowledge that she was looking extremely pretty herself. And then she saw her father walking toward her, deep in conversation with an elderly gentleman. Martha's heart skipped a beat and lurched on. Jefferson's arm was in a sling. She ran to meet him.

"Mon Dieu, Papa, qu'est qu'il y a?" she greeted him in convent French.

Mademoiselle Jeffy

"Il n'y a rien, petite," he assured her, smiling. "It is just a rather stubborn fracture of my wrist. I tripped while walking in the country the other day. This," turning to the old gentleman at his side, "is *Monsieur le Comte de Buffon,* one of the world's greatest naturalists."

Martha hoped she conveyed more interest by her smile and murmured greeting than she felt. At that moment the venerable count and his career as a naturalist were of no interest to her whatever. She wanted to ask questions about that fractured wrist. Was it painful? What did the doctor say? And when could Papa hope to play his violin again? But *Monsieur le Comte* was asking her questions about American wild animals. Had *Mademoiselle* then seen such creatures as the American panther? The great moose? *Non?* Well, then, on and on until Martha could have screamed in exasperation.

Thomas Jefferson never again played his beautiful Amati or wrote with his right hand.

Shortly after his accident he went to the south of France where it was hoped the change of air and the mineral waters would help strengthen the badly knit wrist.

During her father's absence from Paris, Martha re-doubled her efforts with music and Spanish and toiled heroically over a translation of the work of the great Roman historian, Titus Livius. Of this she wrote him:

"*Titus Livius* puts me out of my wits. I cannot read a word by myself, and I read of it very seldom with my master; however, I hope I shall soon be able to take it up again."

The father's reply to this was a long, affectionate letter full of sage advice and a sharp rebuke:

"I do not like your saying that you are unable to read the ancient print of your Livy but with the aid of your master. We are always equal to what we undertake with resolution. . . . It is part of the American character to consider nothing as desperate; to surmount every difficulty by resolution and contrivance."

Martha gathered what comfort she could from this little lecture on perseverance, and began counting the days until his return and word that Polly had reached England safely. Polly and the faithful Isabell Heming would go first to Mrs. John Adams in London, and there they would be called for by a trustworthy steward from the American Embassy in Paris.

Martha found herself daydreaming. She had not seen Polly — suddenly she remembered how long ago she had called her "Little Sistah" — for five years. Polly must be nine now. Would she still have dimples and curls? Would she be as glad to be with them as they were to have her? Martha sighed happily, wondering.

Mademoiselle Jeffy

Polly's decision was quickly made, once the first breath-taking plunge of meeting had successfully been taken.

Why, of course! The very tall gentleman with the firm chin and sudden, unexpected smile was Papa; the lovely young lady with the coppery curls, who spoke French as fluently as she did English, this was Patsy. Polly looked at her sister in big-eyed wonder.

There had been "dear Aunt Eppes" and then "dear Captain Ramsay" and inevitably "dear Mrs. Adams." Polly's whole heart had been given in turn to each preceding recipient of her ardent, headlong devotion. Now she had found two people, and these her very own, upon whom to lavish her affection. To Martha she gave an added childish awe and adoration. Patsy, why, Patsy was practically French!

So Martha took Polly to *Panthémont,* saw her make her curtsy to the *Abbesse* and introduced her to the little girls who would be her classmates. Within a fortnight Polly, whose baptismal name was Mary, was being called Marie by all her French friends, and Marie became one of the names by which she was most frequently called ever afterwards.

Another year sped by and then one day in mid-summer Martha was astonished to hear that a young *Monsieur* was asking for her in the *salon.* Martha put down her book.

"A young *Monsieur* to see *me, Madame?*" Surely there must be some mistake.

"Yes, *Mademoiselle* Jeffy. See, his card."

Martha took the card and read aloud slowly, incredulously, "Thomas Mann Randolph." She paused and a sudden rush of color spread across her throat and cheeks. "Tom — not Tom — no, it can't be — *mais c'est impossible!* Tom Randolph here?" Then she was running down the curving stone steps, crimson skirts billowing and swaying about her.

At the *salon* door she paused to smooth her hair, touch her wide, frilled collar and cuffs. She opened the door softly and went in. Standing at the window with his back to her, was a young man who at a glance she realized was as tall as or taller than her father. He was wearing scarlet breeches and a long-waisted, fawn-colored coat. Under one arm he carried a tri-cornered hat, and lace ruffs made a froth about his coat cuffs. His hair was powdered and tied fashionably in a "club" on his neck.

So this was Tom Randolph, the distant cousin whom she had not seen for almost ten years. Martha cleared her throat softly.

Young Randolph wheeled about. Martha started forward. Both stopped short, and then in the mind of each, like a match struck unexpectedly in a dark room, there

bloomed the same thought: How charming! And to think we've really known each other for years!

For only an instant the spell held, then broke, and Tom Randolph and Martha Jefferson met in a little rush of laughter and interrupted exclamations and clasped hands.

"Patsy, on my honor, you're beautiful!"

"Tom, don't be a goose!" But Martha's cheeks were scarlet and her breath came in little gusts which only heightened her embarrassment. "Come, do sit down and tell me when you arrived." She motioned him to a chair and took one opposite. Could he, she wondered in a panic, hear the wild thumping of her heart? And why, oh, why must her face burn as though she were a scullery maid but recently raking hot ashes?

Mechanically she put her hands to her cheeks to cool their burning and as she did, her eyes encountered Tom's. A roguish grin lit up his handsome, boyish face.

"Remember the kitten you gave me, Patsy?"

"Kitten . . .? Oh, of course! At *Monticello* when I was a little girl. Whatever did you do with it? And what a parting gift! A squirming, mewing kitten for a boy traveling on horseback!"

"Not at all!" Tom took from his pocket a letter which he unfolded. He ran his eyes over the first page, turned the sheet and held up an admonitory finger. "Here, listen to this — I've just finished at the University of Edinburgh, you know. I'm on my way home to Virginia now. This is a letter from my sister. Listen. She says here:

'As I write, Pat lies purring at my feet, looking into the fire. Aside from the loss of a few teeth and an occasional spell of asthma, the old puss is as well and as handsome as ever he was.'"

"Tom, you don't mean to tell me that this is the kitten?"

He nodded, laughing. "The same, and why not? And the handsomest cat in all Virginia."

They had not heard the approach of *Madame l'Abbesse*. It was an iron-clad rule of *Panthémont* that the portress should announce all callers to the venerable *Abbesse* as well as to the friends upon whom they called. Now she stood smiling in the doorway and Martha, hastening to present Tom, knew the little visit was over.

True, the tête-a-tête at *Panthémont* had ended. However, Martha and Thomas Randolph were to meet again and that almost immediately. Thomas Jefferson's hospitable doors were flung wide to welcome his young kinsman. Dinner at the American Embassy was followed by an outing on the Seine, and then young Mr. Randolph presented his compliments and requested the pleasure of

Miss Jefferson and Mr. Jefferson's company at dinner at a celebrated restaurant in the *Bois de Boulogne*.

For a fortnight Martha lived in a world of magic. Then Thomas Randolph was gone, bound for Havre and the ship which would carry him to America. Martha learned of his going unexpectedly and in roundabout ways. Tom gone? She could not believe it.

But no word of farewell? No note just to say they would meet again?

None.

Chapter VIII

TWO DECISIONS FOR PATSY

"I SHALL miss Tom Randolph," Jefferson observed when Martha and Polly dined at the Embassy the following Sunday. "He vowed he'd miss us too, and I make no doubt he will." He smiled broadly down the table at Martha who was applying herself diligently to her soup.

"When think you he'll reach America, Papa?" she asked after a moment to make sure her voice would be quite steady.

"With favorable winds I should say within a month. A fine lad, one of the best, and a really brilliant student from all I hear."

Polly laid down her spoon. "I do not like Tom Randolph," she announced slowly and distinctly, "because he was rude to Patsy."

"Polly Jefferson, please!" Annoyance and embarrassment turned Martha's flushed cheeks a deeper red.

"But he was, wasn't he? He didn't come to say goodby or anything. I think that's being dreadfully rude. He. . . ."

"Come now, don't forget that Tom left hurriedly," Jefferson interrupted. "His ship's sailing date was changed almost without warning. I'm sure he had every intention of taking leave of all his friends, but probably there was no time. Tom's a gentleman, Poll. He wouldn't intentionally be rude to anyone."

But Martha was not comforted, though she took care that no one, least of all loyal little Polly, should suspect her unhappiness. She redoubled her efforts in Spanish and music, and astonished *Madame l'Abbesse* frequently by attending Mass.

Summer made way for autumn, and then such a winter as Paris never had known, settled over the French capital. For the first time within memory there was skating on the Seine; and at Versailles, the Court in masque and costume, frolicked in a winter carnival. But the poor of Paris were not in a carnival mood. In tattered groups they huddled, shivering, on street corners and in alleys, around bonfires built of rubbish. Hungry children cried for bread. And there was no bread. It was rumored the Queen had remarked laughingly, "Then let them eat cake!"

Saddened, horrified, and still brooding over Tom Randolph's discourtesy, Martha spent more and more time in the convent chapel. At Mass and at afternoon Benediction she sat or knelt quietly, letting the solemn beauty of the ritual sweep over her like a healing wind, leaving her comforted. Again, she would go alone, when the only sounds were the petal-like fluttering of the many votive lights and the distant twittering of sparrows high in the eaves. The enmities and hatreds and deceptions of man toward man seemed unreal and far away. Here was peace.

At just this time two deeply religious young girls, postulants, whom Martha knew slightly, took their first vows as novices. Looking at their serene young faces, sensing something of their deep, spiritual joy, Martha made a sudden resolution. That night she wrote to her father. She was staying at *Panthémont;* she, too, would be a nun.

Thomas Jefferson read the letter twice, took up his quill to answer it, then thought of a more direct reply. Several days later the Embassy carriage again stood at the latticed gate where four years earlier it had stopped to admit Martha as a pupil. But, unlike that humid afternoon in August, the March day sparkled with cool sunshine and the plane trees were putting forth their first delicate tracery of green.

For more than an hour the carriage waited. In the convent *salon* Thomas Jefferson was explaining to *Madame l'Abbesse* that he needed his daughters at home with him, that soon they would all be returning to America. His decision, he admitted, had been sudden, but now if *Mademoiselle Marthe* and *Mademoiselle Marie* could be summoned, he would take them with him. He had the highest regard for *Panthémont* and for its teachers. Now, however, he felt his home required the presence of his daughters.

Years later Martha was to hear that, though *Panthémont* was spared by the Revolution as an institution of education, the nuns were scattered and many of them, *Madame* de Taubenheim among them, had died.

Today only the lovely chapel remains standing, at 106 *rue de Grénelle*. It is called *L'Église de Panthémont* and though some aspects of its interior have changed, the same peace and quiet are there which long ago brought comfort to Martha Jefferson.

Thomas Jefferson never referred to the letter which had been directly responsible for ending Martha and Polly's school days in France. Nor could Martha bring herself to mention it. Remorse over her own weakness kept her silent. That she, Patsy Jefferson, should have acted on impulse, should have considered running away from her problem instead of facing it, this seemed impossible to her now. Honestly she faced the knowledge that hers had not been a vocation to be fulfilled; rather it had been a purely emotional escape. The impact of that knowledge on Martha's sensitive nature was shattering.

How could she have done such a thing? How could she have planned to desert her father who daily seemed to rely more and more upon her for companionship? Thus, to the storm of hurt pride already raging in her heart on Tom Randolph's account, Martha added a tempest of self-accusation.

Polly, wholly unaware of anything unusual except the delightful freedom from lessons for the time being at least, flitted about the Embassy, curls flying, dimples twinkling. She wheedled Callie into making "Stage Planks," those molasses cookies dear to the heart of all Southern children, and stood by, sampling each batch as it was taken from the oven.

Polly's natural gayety struck a responsive chord in the hearts of the French servants on the Embassy staff. They adored her and were never so happy as when they had succeeded in coaxing her to perform her little *jeu*. This was the impersonation of the major-domo who took himself and one of his duties, that of announcing guests, very, very seriously.

Throwing open the kitchen door, shoulders hunched high, head flung back, eyes trained perilously on the tip of her nose, Polly would advance two paces stiffly, click her heels and announce in a high, sing-song voice: *"Mademoiselle Marie Jeff-air-son de Monticello, Virginie, États Unis."* Then she would step aside and *"Mademoiselle Jeff-air-son"* would enter, mincing, simpering, bowing to right and left: *"Bonjour, Mesdames — Bonjour, Messieurs."*

A round of applause, handclapping and "Bravo-s" always followed Polly's performance and her ears were quick to catch the spoken flattery intended for them. Only Callie did not applaud, and one day she spoke her mind.

"Miss Polly, honey, please don' act like dat," she admonished gently, shaking her head. Polly had followed her to the linen room where she was mending the ripped lace on Martha's petticoat.

"Why not, Callie?" she asked, running her fingers up and down the rounded edges of a pile of freshly laundered sheets. "Why not? It's ever so much fun, and 'Toinette and Josephine and Margot and Paul and Charles and . . . and the others think so, too. Why not, Callie?" Polly swung her foot in embarrassment and annoyance.

Callie smoothed the fine seam she had made, searching for words. Then: "I know it's fun, l'il Miss, but yo' papa is a great man an' you an' Miss Patsy's his chillun. Dat means you is ladies, *great* ladies, quality. An' no quality folks go cuttin' capers in de kitchen wif de servants. It ain't nice. Yo papa'd be mighty sad if he knew 'bout all dis yere carryin' on, an' so would yo sweet mamma . . . jus' like I's sad 'bout it."

Polly pouted, her lower lip thrust out, her foot still swinging. Callie went on quietly with her work. Then with a rush Polly's arms were around her neck and Polly's flushed face was buried on her starched bosom.

Callie's hand patted the dark curls, and a smile, tender and grateful and understanding, lit up her kind face. In simple faith she had done what she felt was right, and her reward was sweet.

With the coming of winter, tutors were engaged and Martha continued her Spanish and French and again took up her lessons with *Monsieur* Balbastre. Polly reluctantly committed several of La Fontaine's fables to memory and began translating Caesar. Determined to overcome the last vestige of her despondency, Martha worked with relentless concentration. And, as though to put its stamp of approval on such admirable self-discipline, Fate made a sudden, unexpected reward.

It was on a certain March morning that Martha stopped beside the table in the *foyer* on which were piled the Embassy despatch boxes and mail bag. At the same moment the door of Thomas Jefferson's office opened and Mr. Short, his secretary, came out.

"Good-morning, Miss Patsy," he greeted her. "I was just about to take in the mail. There should be some from the States . . . two ships arrived last week. If you'll wait a moment I'll see if there is something for you."

He unlocked the bag and spilled its contents on the table. "Ah, you see? Here is one . . . another . . . and another. I believe that is all."

"Thank you, Mr. Short." Martha picked up the letters. This was from Elisabeth Trist, this from Aunt Carr, and this . . .? Martha looked at the heavy paper; the equally heavy seal that had left a little trail of wax drops behind it on the paper like the tail of a comet; the "M" in "Martha" which was formed by three heavy, vertical lines, with an equally heavy horizontal line laid across the top. Who . . .? And suddenly she knew.

In her room, the door locked against intrusion as she read, joy filled Martha's heart until she felt it could hold

Two Decisions for Patsy

no more. Having read Tom Randolph's letter once she must read it again, and then a third time to make sure of certain implications. There had been a letter enclosed with flowers sent to her on the day of his departure. He had counted the weeks, waiting for her reply. None had come. Now he was writing again. Surely this time she would answer; and upon her word depended his whole life's happiness. He was, to that life's end, her "obedient and faithful servant, Thomas Mann Randolph."

Martha folded the letter and sat down weakly. Why, we've *both* been waiting all these months, she thought. Now when will a letter reach Tom? What shall I say? Will Papa be pleased?

Life was wonderful. Even Polly's plodding: One — two — three, one — two — three, on the harpsichord across the hall, took on a kind of rare and stately beauty. In the garden below, a gardener was clipping the hedge. Martha longed to open the window and lean out and call down to him that he was doing an unusually fine job of hedge-clipping.

With all the aching tension about her heart so suddenly relieved, she knew that now she could explain to her father all the wretchedness that had motivated the writing of the letter at *Panthémont*. She wanted to run now to his office and explain it all, even though matters of international importance must wait. Instead, she opened her desk and sat down to write the letter for which Tom Randolph had waited so long.

Spring in Paris was unusually lovely that year of 1789. The city and the country roundabout shone with a soft radiance, as though Nature were trying to prove to a profligate Court and a hungry, threatening populace that the greatest gifts bestowed by Providence upon mankind are free to all classes.

Gayer, faster whirled the fêtes at Versailles. "Time is short . . . time is short . . . time is short," wailed the fiddles and the flutes and drums. And above the brassy laughter of trumpets and horns could be heard the cry, "Bread, bread, bread for our children, for Mercy's sake!"

At the American Embassy, Thomas Jefferson curbed his impatience as best he could while he waited for a letter from the Congress, granting him a six-months leave of absence. For many months he had waited. He was very tired; he longed for the sight of *Monticello* on its mountain top; his mission to France was finished for the present at least. He was fond of young Thomas Randolph and the knowledge that Martha's romance had taken a happy turn filled him with deep satisfaction. Now to be home again, home in Virginia, surrounded by his family and friends, to resume the life of a Southern planter; this was the American Minister's fervent wish.

It was uppermost in his thoughts when, early one evening he and Polly and Martha strolled about the Embassy garden. The weather was warm for May; lilacs were shedding their purple bugles upon the packed gravel paths, and giant irises in full bloom gave off a heavy, bitter-sweet, mid-summer scent.

"For all of the magnificance of this poor Court of France, it has not half the beauty of *Monticello*," he said gravely, as though thinking aloud.

Martha had broken off a branch of lilac and had buried her face in the blossoms. She looked up quickly. "Why do you say 'This *poor* Court of France,' Papa?" she asked.

Jefferson spoke to Martha as freely and as confidentially as he would have addressed her mother. Now he watched Polly run to the fountain, bent on locating a bull-frog drumming in the vicinity, before he answered. Then:

"I call it poor because, through its own stupid blundering and blindness, it has, I fear, brought itself and with it many innocent people to the brink of tragedy and ruin."

"Just what will happen, think you, Papa? I know that the States-General, when it met last week at Versailles, was thought to have taken some of the King's power and authority from him. Yet the people seem to be loyal enough to him — people one hears talking at the draper's and the hairdresser's. It's strange, isn't it?''

"Yes, Patsy, but then human nature itself is passing strange. *Louis is an honest, unambitious man, who desires neither money nor power for himself.** He is kind and gentle, but his judgment is bad and his will is weak and he is often misunderstood."

"And the Queen, Papa? I remember," Martha laughed, suddenly recalling, "how little Elisabeth Trist always used to speak of her as 'the beautiful, sinful Queen of France. Funny, fat, little Elisabeth! Is Marie Antoinette that . . . 'beautiful and sinful,' Papa?''

The silence that followed her question lengthened until Martha wondered whether her father had thought her presumptuous. She looked up to find him smiling.

"I had been saving a little surprise for you," he said finally, "but since you've come so close to it, I may as well tell you. The Queen, I am certain is not, as Elisabeth described her, 'sinful.' She has been a very extravagant, reckless, headstrong, thoughtless woman in the past years. As to her beauty, you shall judge that for yourself, Patsy, for you're going to see her."

"I? I . . . see the Queen? Why, Papa!" Martha stopped

* Thomas Jefferson's own words in a letter to John Jay — June 17, 1789.

Two Decisions for Patsy

in her tracks and sat down abruptly on a stone bench beside her. Her father smiled down at her.

"Until this year you've been too young to be formally presented at Court," he answered. "My heart is set on having you add that experience to your years in France. The Court of Louis XVI and Marie Antoinette, I doubt not, will go down in history as one of the most sumptuous of all time, also one of the most regrettable. I want you to see it, though even now some of its brilliance is dulled."

Martha's eyes were dark with excitement, her voice almost a whisper. "Oh, Papa . . . I remember when I was a little girl at *Monticello* I used to dream of seeing it all. Now I'm really going to! When will the — the audience be?"

" 'Twill not be an audience in the usually accepted sense, Pat. Formal presentations have been discontinued. However, on the 20th there will be a small formal reception at the Palace which I must attend. This morning I received word from the Court Chamberlain that I may bring you with me. We shall be with the Lafayettes and the de Cornys and some of the others whom you've met here, so there will be no cause for embarrassment. Meanwhile, the Marquise will advise you about Court conduct and dress. It will be an experience to remember always."

Dusk had fallen and the air was suddenly cool. In a

surge of happiness and gratitude, Martha linked her arm in her father's and rubbed her cheek against his shoulder.

"You've always planned such wonderful things for me, Papa," she said softly. "Even this, with all your other worries — that I may see the Palace and the King and Queen."

Smelling faintly of fish, Polly joined them at that moment in a small cloud of gravel dust and took her father's other arm. "A blight on that silly frog!" she panted. "I searched and searched in the fountain for him but all I could get my hands on were goldfish!"

Chapter IX

AU REVOIR TO FRANCE

RAIN hissed against the carriage windows and clung in rows of golden beads across the lamps. In her cloak of sapphire-colored brocade, Martha sat stiffly in her corner, her cheeks flaming, her hands icy. She knew she had been beautiful when she had joined her father in the *salon*. His beaming, "Well, well, well!" would have been proof enough if Polly, Callie, and the dressmaker's assistant who had come to dress her and arrange the flowers in her hair, had not all told her so earlier in the evening.

Au Revoir to France

"Patsy, I vow you look like an angel!" Polly declared from the bed where she was curled up, silently watching.

"Wish yo' sweet mamma could see you, Miss Patsy, honey," had been Callie's comment as she snapped the heavy clasps of that mother's bracelets around the slender wrists.

The dressmaker's assistant plucked a segment of air with her thumb and first finger, kissed it and released it in the French gesture of admiration.

"*Mademoiselle est tout-a-fait exquise — mais exquise!*" she murmured, backing away, head on one side, black eyes sparkling with frank delight in the picture she had helped create.

Martha's hair was strained back and up in an elaborate pompadour, then fastened smoothly at the back of her head, leaving two curls to curve down across her left shoulder. A small wreath of white rosebuds sat jauntily atop the pompadour.

A gown of creamy satin left slim, young shoulders bare, and fell, lace-garlanded, in heavy folds over wide hoops to the floor.

Excitement had made the gray-green eyes dark, and Martha's cheeks were like roses.

"Do I look nice, Papa?" she asked, turning slowly before her father as he held her cloak.

"So *very* nice, my Patsy, that our country may be proud, indeed, of its beautiful representative at the Court of France," he answered with smiling gallantry and carefully kissed her warm cheek. This radiant young creature was Patsy, the same little Patsy for whom he had played his violin on a long ago summer afternoon at *Monticello*. For an instant he saw it all again: the music rack, his own invention, that turned so easily at a touch; his violin under his chin and, over its polished surface, the sudden vision of the tiny, shift-clad figure in the doorway. Was it possible?

Now the carriage was entering a large stone-paved courtyard, was wheeling into line behind other conveyances. The wet night resounded to the clatter of hoofs, the shouts of coachmen and sedan-chair bearers, all intent on maneuvering into better positions. Liveried link boys darted through the melee, their flambeaux sputtering and smoking in the downpour.

Time was growing short. The reception began promptly at ten. Royalty did not wait. Martha wondered nervously as their carriage inched slowly forward, what would happen if the hour struck and they were still out in the rainy night.

But there was time and to spare and presently Martha, her cloak laid aside, was walking beside her father across

Au Revoir to France

a vast corridor in what might well have been a palace in a fairy tale. Great expanses of white marble stretched on every side, reflected and repeated in paneled mirrors that reached from floor to ceiling. Marble staircases curved gracefully upward, to be lost in lofty archways. Thousands of candles fluttered their golden buds of light in crystal chandeliers. Somewhere harps and violins played softly.

Martha observed proudly how many of the distinguished people all about them spoke to her father or tried to get his attention. Soon they were joined by the Lafayettes and entered a somewhat smaller gallery which was already filled with people who, like themselves, had come to see the King and Queen of France.

Without formality yet by design, the assemblage stood, lining the two long walls of the gallery. Martha did not notice when the doors by which they had entered were closed, but suddenly the buzz of conversation died away as doors at the opposite end of the gallery opened.

The King and Queen entered, the Queen with a lady in waiting, Louis with a gentleman of the Court. The Queen turned to the right, the King to the left as they entered, and each began walking slowly forward, stopping to speak for a moment to each person waiting in line. The ladies curtsied, the gentlemen bowed.

The Jeffersons were placed about midway down the

right side, and by turning her head ever so slightly, Martha could watch the slow, stately progress of the Queen as she approached.

Across the gallery, Louis XVI, too, moved along the line. Watching him, Martha thought, What a strange, shuffling walk for such a big man! And he squints as though his eyes hurt. She watched him as he bent to speak to an old lady, saw his great shoulders shake with quiet laughter, and thought, He's kind; his intentions are good. Can he possibly know how many people hate him just because he is the King?

So intent was she upon the King that she had forgotten the Queen. Now suddenly a voice spoke almost at her elbow.

"Ah, Monsieur Jeff-air-son!"

Martha turned and caught her breath. Queen Marie Antoinette stood smiling at her father and he was bending over her hand. Golden hair, rather full blue eyes, straight slender little nose, enchanting smile, and the most beautiful speaking voice Martha knew she had ever heard — all this she took in at a first sweeping estimate.

While Thomas Jefferson and the Queen chatted, Martha continued to gaze. I wish I could know her, *really* know her, she thought. But all I can do is stand and look at her, remembering all the things I've heard about her. *She is Marie Antoinette* whom I've always dreamed about as being a sort of fairy-tale Queen. And she is. But she looks tired and worried and, under all the rouge and rice powder, there are dreadful lines around her eyes as though she'd been crying. I wonder if it is true that her little son is crippled and cannot live long. I wonder what she is really like. Is she truly gracious, and sweet, and gentle, as she seems to be? Or is she the terrible person some people say she is, who does not know the meaning of thoughtfulness or of pity? Who thinks the common people are no better than animals? What true?

In her absorption Martha had inclined her head forward and something of her intense feeling must have communicated itself to the Queen. She turned and Jefferson put his hand on his daughter's arm. Martha curtsied and heard her name spoken, and then the same low voice, saying in French:

"One hears you were a pupil at *L'Abbaye Royal de Panthémont, Mademoiselle.* A beautiful place. When you return to America do not forget its good teaching. Patience — humility — faith . . . those are needful to a happy life."

With a quick little gesture she touched Martha's hand,

and even while the startled girl was murmuring, "Yes, Your Royal Highness," she swept slowly on and was speaking to someone else.

The magic moment had passed, but through the hours that followed when she danced the minuet and the new *pavane,* the question, "What is true?" continued to nag at Martha's generous heart.

The spring days passed, full of gayety and new diversions. The de Cornys gave a ball; Lady Caroline Tufton a supper party for twenty; the lovely Marquise de Lafayette a boating picnic on the Seine. And yet over all one sensed a tension. The very air crackled with it. Oddly enough, it reminded Martha of *Monticello* on the morning of her mother's death before the silence was broken by the sudden terrible wailing of the Negroes.

More letters came from Virginia, ardent, urgent, romantic letters demanding now that a wedding day be set. In late June Martha's answer was given. As soon as they returned to America she would marry Tom Randolph. And the Congress, as though eager to expedite matters, finally sent Thomas Jefferson the long awaited leave of absence. He was free now to go home at last. Another month would be required to clear his desk of pending business.

The three Jeffersons, not to mention Callie, were in a

very ferment of happy anticipation. They were going home!

"I'll go straight to my dear Aunt Eppes's house!" carolled Polly.

"We'll ride again early in the morning, won't we, Papa? Up to our high plateau?" Martha questioned, seeing again the forest bridle paths of *Monticello* winding through the mists of the unreal world of day-break.

"We'll be back at *Monticello, Patsy,* the dearest spot on earth. I've not thought beyond that."

Nearby a soft voice spoke. "Bless God, we's goin' home, Mas' Tom!" Callie brushed tears of joy from her eyes.

On a sultry Sunday evening in mid-July, Martha sat at her desk near the open window, trying to write a letter to Elisabeth Trist. The air was heavy and lifeless. Polly was in bed and asleep. An oblong pattern of light across the lawn below indicated that the American Minister was busy in his office, an unusual thing on a Sunday evening.

All through the afternoon traffic had been heavy on the road leading to Versailles. Now and then the sound of voices shouting had penetrated beyond the Embassy walls. Martha had been aware of it without actually giving it much thought. Her father had entertained diplomats at supper and Callie had brought trays upstairs for her and Polly. Now she realized that all the events of the day were forming a pattern: something sinister was happening. But what?

The night was very dark, very still — so still that she could hear through the open window her father's papers crackle as he moved them on his desk downstairs. Martha laid down her quill and walked to the window. Crickets chirred; the fountain splashed coolly in the dark. In spite of the oppressive heat, Martha shivered and turned back to the lighted room.

Midway she stopped, listening. From the direction of the city came a confusion of sounds — were they shots? Cannonading? Then one sound detached itself from the rest and grew in volume. A horse, galloping at a killing pace, was racing toward Versailles. Nearer, nearer it came — passed — disappeared in the dark. Though Martha was not aware of it, she had heard the *Duc de Liancourt* speeding to the Palace, carrying an historic message to the King. The Bastille had fallen. The head of the governor was being carried on a pike in triumph through the streets. No longer was the sound of the drums of revolution a faint, distant rumble. With a deafening roar it broke over the nation. The French Revolution had begun.

For the rest of the summer Paris was in constant disorder. Old friends exchanging political views, were suddenly enemies. Many shops catering to the patronage of the nobility were stoned, looted and finally closed. Martha abandoned plans for trousseau shopping and seldom left the cool peace and quiet of the Embassy garden. Whenever she did venture forth in the carriage behind her father's handsome, mettlesome bays, she returned depressed and unhappy. Hunger and desperate want were changing the merry expression on the beautiful face of Paris to a grimace of savage hatred for anything or anyone representing the aristocracy. Was there something one could do to help? Apparently nothing — but watch the frightful object lesson being taught with such deadly thoroughness: the lesson of thoughtless greed being overcome by its own folly.

It was September before the Jeffersons finally left Paris. At Havre they were detained by autumn storms which already had begun. Finally they crossed the English Channel to Cowes where they had disembarked five years earlier, and sailed aboard the *Clermont* for America.

Two members of the party faced the voyage with practically unreserved joy. Both Callie and eleven-year-old Polly accepted the probability of gales with resignation. They were homeward bound, so what mattered the turmoil in the foreign land they just had left?

But, standing in a sheltered corner of the deck as the *Clermont* plowed steadily through the choppy seas, Martha

and her father often spoke of France and wondered what would be the outcome of its present tragedy. Warmhearted Liberal that he was, Thomas Jefferson agreed enthusiastically in the change of government from that of a Monarchy to a Democracy. That this could be accomplished without bloodshed he never had doubted; that quite the opposite was the case, filled him with lasting sorrow.

"But if the — common people hate *all* nobility, *all* aristocracy, without stopping to question what their views may be, will not some of our dearest friends — people like the de Cornys and the Lafayettes and *Monsieur* de Buffon — will not they suffer along with the rest?" Wrapped in a heavy, hooded cape, Martha shouted above the screaming of the wind in the sails and the crash of waves against the ship. Like her father, she had become a good sailor.

"Possibly, quite possibly. Every great reform has its innocent martyrs, Patsy, as well as its guilty culprits. I pray though that when I return to France in April I shall find our good friends enjoying life there as never before, under a Democracy just as we are beginning to in America." Jefferson's voice was full of optimism and he nodded, smiling happily through the flying spray. Alone, however, he had hours of gravest doubt.

The homeward voyage, unlike the nineteen-day crossing on the *Ceres* five years before, was long and stormy, and it was late November when at last the travelers set foot on American soil — at Norfolk, Virginia.

Eager to be home, suspecting who undoubtedly would be there to welcome her, Martha nevertheless curbed her impatience as best she could while they humored Polly in her plea to stop at "my dear Aunt Eppes's house."

The entire Eppes family welcomed them warmly, but none with the manner of a knight greeting his lady, which was young Jack Eppes's attitude when Polly stood before him. Though she was not yet twelve, Jack, several years older, thought her the most enchanting creature he ever had beheld.

"Remember the day you were shanghaied on Captain Ramsay's ship?" he reminisced, beaming down at her as they stood together before the parlor fire. Behind them, Martha and her father and the Eppeses exchanged family news.

Polly's blue eyes smiled and her dimples twinkled. "Remember it?" she laughed, "La, I'll never forget how I went for poor Captain Ramsay when I found what had happened! Then he showed me how to play 'Cat's Cradle' with a piece of twine and in a moment I'd fallen in love with him! He was a right sweet person, Jack, and he didn't in the least hold it against me that I kicked his shins like

a fiend." Polly's laughter bubbled above the hum of conversation behind them, and she blushed and clapped her
hand over her mouth. What would Aunt Eppes think?
And Papa?

But they seemed not to have noticed and Jack said
gravely, "I fair lost my wits when I found you had gone,
Poll. Believe me, it's fine that you're back again."

Polly agreed and would have stayed happily at *Eppington* for the Christmas festivities had her father permitted.
But Thomas Jefferson was impatient to reach *Monticello,*
and after a few more days of visiting, the travelers were
on their way.

On a day late in December, the heavy coach followed
by the luggage cart, turned in at the gates at the foot
of the mountain. Peering through the misted windows,
Martha thought of the morning she had left *Monticello*
seven years before. It had been just such a day, with snow
falling and a high wind whipping the shrubs and sighing
through the tree tops.

Up, up, and around rolled the coach. Suddenly it lurched
to a stop.

"What is it?" Martha pressed her face close to the
glass, rubbed the steaming surface with her gloved finger-
tips.

Somewhere up ahead there was a hubbub, laughter,

singing, shouting. Jefferson threw open the door and got out. Martha, with Polly's head bobbing excitedly before her, glimpsed her father standing in the wind, his cloak blowing back, arms stretched out in a gesture of welcome, his face working with emotion. Martha was out of the coach in a flash and at his side, and then she felt her own eyes fill with happy tears.

Down the drive came the *Monticello* slaves: house servants, field hands, stable men, carpenters, bricklayers, all running, hands outstretched, shouting, singing snatches of hymns, welcoming their adored "Mas' Tom" and his daughters home.

The horses were unhitched, and rather than hurt these simple, kindly people who loved him so, Jefferson did as they begged: with Martha, he re-entered the coach and let them push and pull it the remaining distance to the house.

To be home, to be so loved after the recent months in an atmosphere of fear and hate, this was sweet. Standing just inside the huge, closed mahogany door, hat in hand, Jefferson paused a moment, looking across the great hall of *Monticello*. Beside him, Martha slipped her hand in his. Across this wide hall she had hurried that afternoon so long ago when, wakened from her nap, she had heard the music of his violin. He would not play again, but the memory

of that afternoon's happiness would be in both their hearts
always.

"Let's explore, Patsy!" Polly broke the spell. "Let's
start right now, this very instant!" Impatiently her fingers
tugged at the buttons of her coat. "I reckon I was much
too young when I went to Aunt Eppes's to remember much
about this house. My, but it's big and beautiful!"

But Martha waved impetuous Polly off, laughing. "Tomorrow, darling," she promised. "Let's get our breath a
bit first. There's enough to see here to keep us busy for
the rest of the winter. Come, we've just time to freshen up
before supper."

They were lingering over the meal — Southern baked
ham and collard greens and beaten biscuit with muscadine
jelly — when there came a knocking at the great door.
A moment later the butler announced, "Mas' Tom Randolph."

Martha's feet seemed skimming along on air. At the
drawing-room door she paused, breathless. The waiting
was over. Tom had come. Tom was here.

Tom Randolph stood looking down at the keyboard
of Mrs. Jefferson's Forte-piano, soundlessly spacing octaves.
A slight movement in the doorway attracted his attention.
He looked up, and then again, as at *Panthémont,* they were
running to meet each other.

"Patsy! My Patsy darling!"

"Tom . . . oh, Tom. . . ."

Then he took her in his arms.

The following day, still moving in a rosy haze of happiness, Martha kept her promise to Polly. Together, while their father was closeted with the overseer, the sisters wandered through the mansion. Polly was no more astonished and delighted at much they discovered than was Martha herself.

"Look," Martha said, pointing upward as they stood in a narrow passage between Jefferson's bedroom and his study. "During the day Papa has his bed pulled up and out of the way so that he has this open passage between the two rooms. At night it is let down. I'd forgotten."

"And if he can't sleep and wants to read at night, all he has to do is step out on the study side, light a candle and choose a book," Polly finished saucily, smiling up at her tall sister. "I declare, Patsy, that's the most wonderful thing I ever heard of. Think of sleeping in two rooms at once!"

Martha rumpled Polly's curls and gave her a quick hug. "You precious goose," she laughed. "Only you would think of that. But Papa didn't plan it for such an exciting reason, I'm afraid. I remember hearing him tell one of his friends in Paris that when he planned this house he had bed spaces made as part of the architectural design . . . you know your room and mine both have the built-in beds. And this," she waved toward the ceiling, "does give both of these rooms ever so much more wall space."

At the foot of a narrow flight of ascending stairs Martha paused to describe her encounter with the Baroness de Riedesel. It seemed so long ago . . . part of another life. Where was the kindly, well-meaning baroness now? Polly, however, was mightily entertained. "La, I'd have been frightened out of my wits," she said in a small, awed voice, looking beyond Martha into the shadows as though expecting to see the baroness charging out of them.

"Oh, believe me, I was frightened," Martha admitted. "You see I've never forgotten."

In the reception hall she pointed to the great clock over the door leading to the east portico. "See, dear, a quarter after eleven. Now come here." She opened the door, letting in a blast of wintry air. Polly slipped out to the portico to stand beside her sister for a second, looking up at the duplicate face of the clock.

"Well, fancy!" she exclaimed, shivering happily in the comforting warmth of the hall. "The clock shows on both sides, doesn't it? No need to come indoors to see the time. Goodness, Patsy, our *Monticello* just has everything in the world anyone would want, hasn't it?"

Patsy Jefferson of Monticello

Martha had a fleeting vision of the Palace of Versailles, the American Embassy, the beautiful villas of the de Corneys and the Lafayettes, the magnificent establishments of many of their friends in Paris, and a great wave of pride and gratitude and love for this beloved home of hers swept over her.

"Yes, Polly, *Monticello* is the dearest, most beautiful place in the whole world," she said. "I hope it will be here forever and ever."

Chapter X

MOSAIC OF YEARS

THOMAS JEFFERSON was never to return to his beloved France. Nor was he long to be permitted to remain Farmer Jefferson of *Monticello*. Almost before the family was settled, word came from the Capital in New York that his services were needed there. President George Washington had appointed him Secretary of State. It was an office he did not want but, loving his country as he did, Jefferson could not refuse.

Plans for his move North and for Martha's wedding filled the days. The New Year (1790) came and on February 23, Martha and Thomas Mann Randolph were married.

The following day Jefferson set out on his journey to

New York. Polly went to *Eppington* for a visit and the young people had beautiful *Monticello* to themselves for their honeymoon.

The months and years passed happily, serenely. Martha found her husband a brilliant, high-strung man whose winning manner made it extremely simple for him to make a place for himself in politics. He became a member of the Virginia Senate in 1793. Shortly after their marriage he built a stately plantation house on property he owned a few miles from *Monticello* and there for a brief period he and Martha lived. Soon, however, they were back at *Monticello* and there they remained for many years.

On a December day in 1793, Martha looked up from the picture book she was reading to little Anne Cary Randolph. Across the nursery in front of the fire, old Callie crooned softly to the new baby, Thomas Jefferson Randolph. The mail had just been brought in and, while Anne pointed out objects on the page before her, Martha reached for and opened a letter from Lady Caroline Tufton. It was postmarked London — October. Eagerly Martha broke the seal and began to read. When she had finished reading she set the baby on the floor and hurried from the room, closing the door behind her. She crossed the hall to her own room and, almost running, flung herself into a deep chair and covered her face with her hands.

"No —" she whispered, "no — no — they couldn't have done that! They couldn't!"

Then she smoothed the crumpled letter and read the words again, and as she read she saw Marie Antoinette's smile and felt again the charm of her personality. In Paris Marie Antoinette had been beheaded by the Revolutionists.

Meanwhile, the Capital of the United States had been moved to Philadelphia. Here Thomas Jefferson rented a pleasant dwelling where at once there gathered the best minds, the warmest adherents of Democracy in America.

Stunned and horrified at the unspeakable excesses of the Reign of Terror in France, yet they rejoiced that that beautiful country was free at last. Writing to a friend of the martyrdom of those French members of the nobility and aristocracy in no way sympathetic to the despotism of the Monarchy, Jefferson wrote:

"But time and truth will embalm their memories, while their posterity will be enjoying that very liberty for which they would never have hesitated to offer up their lives. The liberty of the whole earth was depending on the issue of the contest, and was ever such a prize won with so little innocent blood?"

Patsy Jefferson of Monticello

Polly was entered at Mrs. Pine's school in Philadelphia and almost at once struck up a great friendship with President Washington's adopted daughter, Nellie Custis.

At *Monticello* Martha worried over her father's uncongenial labors in Philadelphia. Determined to keep his country a nation guided by the wishes of *all* the people instead of a privileged few, he quarreled bitterly with Alexander Hamilton, the secretary of the Treasury. Then, in the early autumn of 1793 yellow fever broke out in the Capital and Jefferson brought Polly home to *Monticello* and, after a brief stay, returned alone to Philadelphia. By the end of the year, however, he was back on his beloved mountain top where he said, "My private business can never call me elsewhere, and certainly politics will not, which I have ever hated both in theory and practice."

The four years that followed were happy ones for the Jefferson clan. Martha had another little daughter and when not busy with the children she spent much of her time with her father, walking or driving over the rolling miles of the plantation. A new wing was being added to the house, another remodeled. The land, so long neglected, was being re-cultivated. Polly, happiest always with her "dear Aunt Eppes," divided her time between *Monticello* and *Eppington*.

Mosaic of Years

Thomas Jefferson's belief that politics would never again invade his "little mountain" was ill-founded for, in 1796 when Washington refused a third presidential term, John Adams was elected second President of the United States and Thomas Jefferson was elected vice-president.

Again the young Randolphs were master and mistress of *Monticello*. Martha's days were crowded with supervision of the huge household and with the care of her growing family of children. Thomas Randolph was busy from dawn to dusk either in the plantation office or out on the property itself. The up-hill-down-dale miles of forest and farm land required unceasing surveillance. Those rare occasions when Thomas Jefferson could find the time to be at home for a few days or a fortnight, were gala times for the family at *Monticello*. For the children there were his favorite games of Cross-questions and I-love-my-love-with-an-A, in the firelight before candles were lighted, and for Tom and Martha there was always fascinating news from the nation's capital.

Polly, meanwhile, was fast becoming a beauty. Elfin and pretty as a child, at twenty she was lovelier still, with a sparkling wit and magnetism that attracted suitors from the far corners of Virginia and beyond. *Eppington,* however, held her heart, and on October 13, 1797, Maria

Jefferson and her cousin John (Jack) Wayles Eppes were married. Henceforth "my dear Aunt Eppes's house" would be her home.

Two years more and then Thomas Jefferson was elected President of the United States. Martha, reading over her husband's shoulder the letter bringing the news, found her heart racing.

"Why, Tom, he's alone! He'll want *some* of us there with him for the inauguration! When will it be — March? I'm going!"

Not since the long ago day when he had turned to find her standing in the doorway of the *salon* at *Panthémont* had Thomas Randolph seen that look of deep joy and wonder in Martha's eyes.

"But Patsy, the children — what of them? Remember, the capital's in Washington now, and a very mud hole they say it is, in the middle of a forest. And the journey for you, dear. No, it's not a journey I'd have my wife take with the roads hub-deep in spring mud. 'Tis a mad idea."

Martha's husband spoke with his usual brisk air of finality, but for once he met a will as strong as his own.

"Your wife, aye, Tom," Martha spoke softly but with inflexible determination, "but Thomas Jefferson's daughter, too. *I'm going to Washington.* As for the children, I'll see they're in good hands. Mary, Nell, Jimmie and Ellen can stay happily here with their mammies — perhaps Aunt Carr will come up for a fortnight. Anne and Jeff shall go with me. Nine and ten — a wonderful age — they'll never forget it. "Come, Tom," she put her hands on his shoulders, leaned to kiss the stubborn line of his jaw — "'twill be something to remember always. You come, too!'"

But early spring planting could not be left to overseer and farm hands. So, on a February day, Mrs. Randolph, with her ten-year-old daughter, Anne, and her nine-year-old son, Jeff, set out in the Jefferson coach for the nation's new Capital. Two of *Monticello's* most trusted drivers were on the box and Callie rode with her mistress.

To the children it was the gayest adventure. There was a stop at Mount Vernon for an overnight visit with Mrs. Washington who must hear all about Polly's new baby, little Francis Eppes. The General himself seemed very near; awestruck, Jeff touched his hero's spectacle case.

In the morning they were again on their way, bumping, rumbling over the rutty road to Washington. A rider had been sent ahead to announce the arriving guests.

It was shortly before noon when the coach drew up before Conrad's boarding house, where the President Elect still made his home. Not until after the Inauguration on March 3rd, still several days off, would he move to the

Patsy Jefferson of Monticello

President's Palace, later to be known as the White House.

Scarcely had the coach stopped when Anne and Jeff were tumbling out to go racing into the outstretched arms of "Gran'pa." Martha followed, to be included in the embrace. Any uncertainties she might have felt regarding her father's wanting them were dispelled by his welcome. In spite of the seething turmoil about him, he seemed not to want his family out of his sight.

"Patsy, Patsy child," he said when at last they were all safely behind the closed doors of her sitting room, "who but you would have guessed what it means to me to have you all here!"

Young Jeff, leaning against his chair, suddenly slid his arm around his grandfather's neck. "I'll be your Vice-President, Gran'pa," he asserted gravely. "I'll do all the things you don't have time to get done, being busy making laws."

Jefferson looked at the serious little face under the thatch of sandy hair and patted the hand lying on his knee.

"That's a promise, Jeff," he said. Yet even he could not have foreseen how completely that promise would be kept. From early manhood Thomas Jefferson Randolph took charge of his grandfather's affairs and managed them conscientiously and well.

Patsy Jefferson of Monticello

The Senate Chamber was packed. The Oath of Office had been administered. Now Thomas Jefferson began his Inaugural Address. The first words were lost to Martha in the blur of emotion that swept through her. This was Papa, this tall, gaunt, tired-looking man who had known so many honors, so much bitter grief and criticism.

". . . This is the sum of good government. Equal and exact justice to all men of whatever state or persuasion, a jealous care of the right of election. . . ." (Only yesterday I saw him riding up the driveway and ran to meet him.)

". . . Freedom of religion, freedom of press, freedom of person and trial by juries impartially selected. . . ." (The first time I had ever been on a horse — high and safe on the saddle before him, the wind singing against my bonnet lining — that was another yesterday. Anne is not listening. Jeff is.)

". . . These form the bright constellation which has gone before us and which has guided us in an age of revolution and reformation. The wisdom of our sages, and the blood of our heroes have attained them for us." (The morning we sailed from Boston he was thoughtful of Callie in the withering heat — the girls at *Panthémont* were as much at ease with him and spoke as freely before him as before their own fathers — he respected the tradition of